Academic

Preparation

In Science

Teaching for Transition
From High School
To College

College Entrance Examination Board, New York, 1986

Academic Preparation in Science is one of a series of six books. The Academic Preparation Series includes books in English, the Arts, Mathematics, Science, Social Studies, and Foreign Language. Single copies of any one of these books can be purchased for $6.95. Orders for 5 through 49 copies of a single title receive a 20 percent discount; orders for 50 or more copies receive a 50 percent discount.

A boxed set of all the books in the Academic Preparation Series is available for $20. Orders for five or more sets receive a 20 percent discount. Each set also includes a copy of *Academic Preparation for College: What Students Need to Know and Be Able to Do.*

Payment or purchase order for individual titles or the set should be addressed to: College Board Publications, Box 886, New York, New York 10101.

The discussion of Vee maps and concept maps on pages 65-69 and the accompanying illustrations, Figures 4.4 and 4.5, are based on materials in *Learning How to Learn,* and are reproduced by permission. Copyright © 1984 by Cambridge University Press. Joseph D. Novak and D. Bob Gowin, *Learning How to Learn* (New York: Cambridge University Press, 1984), pp. 1-3, 15-17, 55-63.

The instructional sequence on plant competition on pages 71-77 is adapted from a unit developed by the Chelsea Science Simulation Project and used by permission. Copyright © 1982 by Chelsea College. M.E. Leveridge, *Chelsea Science Simulations Competition COMPETE* (London: Edward Arnold, 1982), student leaflet, pp. 1-8. Distributed by CONDUIT, University of Iowa–Oakdale Campus, Iowa City, Iowa.

The material titled "The Web of Life," which is reproduced as Appendix B and is also adapted for use in the text on pages 81-84 and in the accompanying illustrations, Figures 5.3–5.7, is taken from BSCS Green Version, *Biological Science: An Ecological Approach,* and used by permission. Copyright © 1963 by the American Institute of Biological Sciences, copyright © 1968 by The Regents of the University of California. *Biological Science: An Ecological Approach,* 2d ed., Biological Sciences Curriculum Study (BSCS) Green Version (Chicago: Rand McNally, 1968), pp. 18-20.

ISBN: 0-87447-223-7

9 8 7 6 5 4 3 2 1

Contents

Figures and Tables

Principal Writer and Consultant

Leopold E. Klopfer, Professor of Education, School of Education, and Senior Scientist, Learning Research and Development Center, University of Pittsburgh

Science Advisory Committee, 1984–85

Michael A. Saltman, Chairman, Science Department, Bronxville School, New York (*Chair*)

Edward J. Finn, Professor of Physics, Georgetown University, Washington, D.C.

John W. Macklin, Assistant Professor of Chemistry, University of Washington, Seattle

Naomi Martin, Coordinator of Secondary Mathematics/Science, Horry County School District, Conway, South Carolina

Joann M. Meyer, Assistant Science Department Chairman for Biology, Dulles High School, Sugar Land, Texas

Jonathan Reiskind, Associate Professor of Zoology, University of Florida, Gainesville

Robert E. Yager, Professor of Science Education, University of Iowa, Iowa City

Acknowledgments

The College Board wishes to thank all the individuals and organizations that contributed to *Academic Preparation in Science*. In addition to those who served on the Science Advisory Committee and the Council on Academic Affairs, explicit acknowledgment should be accorded to Perry Turner, Cheryl Simon, Yola Coffeen, Mary Carroll Scott, and Carol J. Meyer. Without the leadership of Adrienne Y. Bailey, vice president for Academic Affairs at the College Board, this book would not have assumed its present form. Although none of these people is individually responsible for the contents of the book, the Educational EQuality Project owes much to their efforts.

James Herbert, General Editor

The College Board is a nonprofit membership organization that provides tests and other educational services for students, schools, and colleges. The membership is composed of more than 2,500 colleges, schools, school systems, and education associations. Representatives of the members serve on the Board of Trustees and advisory councils and committees that consider the College Board's programs and participate in the determination of its policies and activities.

The Educational EQuality Project is a 10-year effort of the College Board to strengthen the academic quality of secondary education and to ensure equality of opportunity for postsecondary education for all students. Begun in 1980, the project is under the direction of the Board's Office of Academic Affairs.

For more information about the Educational EQuality Project and inquiries about this report, write to the Office of Academic Affairs, The College Board, 45 Columbus Avenue, New York, New York 10023-6917.

To Our Fellow Teachers of Science

Science teachers have an important opportunity. Too often science is thought of as the work of a small group of specialists, as knowledge open only to a few. We know this should not be the case, but the presumption is strong and students may stay away, or be kept away, because of it. This attitude must be countered in our science classrooms and, we hope, eliminated from our schools and society. If it is not, many students will miss an introduction to knowledge that can be of real personal importance and to a way of thinking that is deeply influential in shaping our understanding of the world and of life itself.

This is not to say that all students can or should become professional scientists. Such, of course, is not the case, and we do not recommend academic preparation that is limited by this view. What we do say, however, and say strongly, is that high school is too early a time to decide that a student has no talent for science or little need for it in his or her education. Our powers of prediction are not, and never will be, sure enough to permit such conclusions in justice. Good sense about what individuals need to know to succeed in college and in life does not tell us so in fact.

Moreover, we believe that giving thought and effort to how *all* students can profit from the science classroom will also strengthen that classroom for each student in it. Asking what any student needs to know and be able to do should lead us toward shared understandings about what is essential in the body of scientific knowledge and to making hard but necessary decisions about what can be dropped, or given less attention, in our overburdened curriculum. It should also result in a clearer focus on, and direct practice in, the enterprise of empirical inquiry—the hallmark of the natural sciences. It should, that is, help students to grasp that what is distinctive about science is not only its content or findings, but even more so its careful processes of investigation and verification.

Teaching, too, can be a matter of empirical inquiry. The proof of effectiveness is usually not long in coming. Within a day or two, or at most a couple of weeks, teachers have information on how well a lesson, a lab, or an instructional sequence worked for their students. In the long run, such "experimentation" should actually promote more efficient innovation, producing ever better revisions of instructional strategies and materials.

We suggest that the ideas students bring with them often provide a useful place to begin science instruction. Everyone has some curiosity about the material world, some commonsense ideas about how it works. As teachers, we see our work as drawing out and cultivating that interest, as helping students learn how to refine and revise their ideas about natural phenomena. No doubt it has always been easier to succeed with very able students, many of whom are strongly attracted to the content of the sciences. This, of course, contributes to the popular notion that only the most able students can learn science. The notion is incorrect. When instruction is properly designed, science can be accessible to virtually all students.

This book, in short, shares the optimism and persistence of empirical inquiry. In the following pages you will find suggestions for preparing students for college. You will also find discussions of principles pertaining to science education that are derived from research or experience. Chapter 1 describes the relation of this book to the Educational EQuality Project and to its publication, *Academic Preparation for College*. In Chapter 2 we illustrate and elaborate on the science learning that will give students a fair chance to make the most of college. A clear and specific delineation of the kinds of things that science students should be learning to do may help focus instruction on the processes of scientific investigation. Chapter 3 identifies and comments on some principles you may find useful in discussing the science curriculum in your high school or school district. Chapter 4 offers what we hope will be some thought-provoking examples of how instruction can be targeted to specific aspects of science learning, and Chapter 5 suggests how science learning relates to the Basic Academic Competencies—broad intellectual skills that students need for success in all fields of study. In Chapter 6 we identify some general issues we believe merit further discussion.

This entire book, however, is meant to provide suggestions for further discussion and investigation. We hope that you will explore it and return to it, elaborating on parts of it whenever they may be of use in your own work. Think of its suggestions not as dogma but as ideas that can be tested with your own students.

Science Advisory Committee

I. Beyond the Green Book

Identifying the academic preparation needed for college is a first step toward providing that preparation for all students who might aspire to higher education. But the real work of actually achieving these learning outcomes lies ahead.[1]

This book is a sequel to *Academic Preparation for College: What Students Need to Know and Be Able to Do*, which was published in 1983 by the College Board's Educational EQuality Project. Now widely known as the Green Book, *Academic Preparation for College* outlined the knowledge and skills students need in order to have a fair chance at succeeding in college. It summarized the combined judgments of hundreds of educators in every part of the country. The Green Book sketched learning outcomes that could serve as goals for high school curricula in six Basic Academic Subjects: English, the arts, mathematics, science, social studies, and foreign languages. It also identified six Basic Academic Competencies on which depend, and which are further developed by, work in these subjects. Those competencies are reading, writing, speaking and listening, mathematics, reasoning, and studying. The Green Book also called attention to additional competencies in using computers and observing, whose value to the college entrant increasingly is being appreciated.

With this book we take a step beyond *Academic Preparation for College*. The Green Book simply outlined desired results of high school education—the learning all students need to be adequately prepared for college. It contained no specific suggestions about how to achieve those results. Those of us working with the Educational EQuality Project strongly believed—and still believe—that ultimately curriculum and instruction are matters of local expertise

---

1. The College Board, *Academic Preparation for College: What Students Need to Know and Be Able to Do* (New York: The College Board, 1983), p. 31.

4

and responsibility. Building consensus on goals, while leaving flexible the means to achieve them, makes the most of educators' ability to respond appropriately and creatively to conditions in their own schools. Nevertheless, teachers and administrators, particularly those closely associated with the EQuality project, often have asked how the outcomes sketched in the Green Book might be translated into actual curricula and instructional practices—how they can get on with the "real work" of education. These requests in part seek suggestions about how the Green Book goals might be achieved; perhaps to an even greater extent they express a desire to get a fuller picture of those very briefly stated goals. Educators prefer to think realistically, in terms of courses and lessons. Discussion of proposals such as those in the Green Book proceeds more readily when goals are filled out and cast into the practical language of possible courses of action.

To respond to these requests for greater detail, and to encourage further nationwide discussion about what should be happening in our high school classrooms, teachers working with the Educational EQuality Project have prepared this book and five like it, one in each of the Basic Academic Subjects. By providing suggestions about how the outcomes described in *Academic Preparation for College* might be achieved, we hope to add more color and texture to the sketches in that earlier publication. We do not mean these suggestions to be prescriptive or definitive, but to spark more detailed discussion and ongoing dialogue among our fellow teachers who have the front-line responsibility for ensuring that all students are prepared adequately for college. We also intend this book and its companions for guidance counselors, principals, superintendents, and other officials who must understand the work of high school teachers if they are better to support and cooperate with them.

Students at Risk, Nation at Risk

Academic Preparation for College was the result of an extensive grassroots effort involving hundreds of educators in every part of the country. However, it was not published in a vacuum. Since the beginning of this decade, many blue-ribbon commissions and stud-

5

ies also have focused attention on secondary education. The concerns of these reports have been twofold. One, the reports note a perceptible decline in the academic attainments of students who graduate from high school, as indicated by such means as standardized test scores and comments from employers; two, the reports reflect a widespread worry that, unless students are better educated, our national welfare will be in jeopardy. *A Nation at Risk* made this point quite bluntly:

> Our Nation is at risk. Our once unchallenged preeminence in commerce, industry, science, and technological innovation is being overtaken by competitors throughout the world. . . . The educational foundations of our society are presently being eroded by a rising tide of mediocrity that threatens our very future as a Nation and a people.[2]

The Educational EQuality Project, an effort of the College Board throughout the decade of the 1980s to improve both the quality of preparation for college and the equality of access to it, sees another aspect of risk: if our nation is at risk because of the level of students' educational attainment, then we must be more concerned with those students who have been most at risk.

Overall, the predominance of the young in our society is ending. In 1981, as the EQuality project was getting under way, about 41 percent of our country's population was under 25 years old and 26 percent was 50 years old or older. By the year 2000, however, the balance will have shifted to 34 percent and 28 percent, respectively. But these figures do not tell the whole story, especially for those of us working in the schools. Among certain groups, youth is a growing segment of the population. For example, in 1981, 71 percent of black and 75 percent of Hispanic households had children 18 years old or younger. In comparison, only 52 percent of all white households had children in that age category. At the beginning of the 1980s, children from minority groups already made up more than 25 percent of all public school students.[3] Clearly, concern for im-

---

2. National Commission on Excellence in Education, *A Nation at Risk* (Washington, D.C.: U.S. Government Printing Office, 1983), p. 5.

3. Ernest L. Boyer, *High School* (New York: Harper & Row, 1983), pp. 4-5. U.S. Department of Education, National Center for Education Statistics, *Digest of Education Statistics: 1982* (Washington, D.C.: U.S. Government Printing Office, 1982), p. 43.

proving the educational attainments of all students increasingly must involve concern for students from such groups of historically disadvantaged Americans.

How well will such young people be educated? In a careful and thoughtful study of schools, John Goodlad found that "consistent with the findings of virtually every study that has considered the distribution of poor and minority students . . . minority students were found in disproportionately large percentages in the low track classes of the multiracial samples [of the schools studied]."[4] The teaching and learning that occur in many such courses can be disappointing in comparison to that occurring in other courses. Goodlad reported that in many such courses very little is expected, and very little is attempted.[5]

When such students are at risk, the nation itself is at risk, not only economically but morally. That is why this book and its five companions offer suggestions that will be useful in achieving academic excellence for *all* students. We have attempted to take into account that the resources of some high schools may be limited and that some beginning high school students may not be well prepared. We have tried to identify ways to keep open the option of preparing adequately for college as late as possible in the high school years. These books are intended for work with the broad spectrum of high school students—not just a few students and not only those currently in the "academic track." We are convinced that many more students can—and, in justice, should—profit from higher education and therefore from adequate academic preparation.

Moreover, many more students actually enroll in postsecondary education than currently follow the "academic track" in high school. Further, discussions with employers have emphasized that many of the same academic competencies needed by college-bound students also are needed by high school students going directly into the world of work. Consequently, the Educational EQuality Project, as its name indicates, hopes to contribute to achieving a democratic excellence in our high schools.

---

4. John Goodlad, *A Place Called School* (New York: McGraw-Hill, 1984), p. 156.
5. Ibid., p. 159.

The Classroom: At the Beginning
as Well as the End of Improvement

A small book such as this one, intended only to stimulate dialogue about what happens in the classroom, cannot address all the problems of secondary education. On the other hand, we believe that teachers and the actual work of education—that is to say, curriculum and instruction—should be a more prominent part of the nationwide discussion about improving secondary education.

A 1984 report by the Education Commission of the States found that 44 states either had raised high school graduation requirements or had such changes pending. Twenty-seven states had enacted new policies dealing with instructional time, such as new extracurricular policies and reduced class sizes.[6] This activity reflects the momentum for and concern about reform that has been generated recently. It demonstrates a widespread recognition that critiques of education without concrete proposals for change will not serve the cause of improvement. But what will such changes actually mean in the classroom? New course requirements do not necessarily deal with the academic quality of the courses used to fulfill those requirements. Certain other kinds of requirements can force instruction to focus on the rote acquisition of information to the exclusion of fuller intellectual development. Manifestly, juggling of requirements and courses without attention to what needs to occur between teachers and students inside the classroom will not automatically produce better prepared students. One proponent of reform, Ernest Boyer, has noted that there is danger in the prevalence of "quick-fix" responses to the call for improvement. "The depth of discussion about the curriculum . . . has not led to a serious and creative look at the nature of the curriculum. . . . states [have not asked] what we ought to be teaching."[7]

---

6. *Action in the States: Progress toward Education Renewal*, A Report by the Task Force on Education for Economic Growth (Denver, Colorado: Education Commission of the States, 1984), p. 27.

7. In Thomas Toch, "For School Reform's Top Salesmen, It's Been Some Year," *Education Week*, June 6, 1984, p. 33.

Such questioning and discussion is overdue. Clearly, many improvements in secondary education require action outside the classroom and the school. Equally clearly, even this action should be geared to a richer, more developed understanding of what is needed in the classroom. By publishing these books we hope to add balance to the national debate about improving high school education. Our point is not only that it is what happens between teachers and students in the classroom that makes the difference. Our point is also that what teachers and students do in classrooms must be thoughtfully considered before many kinds of changes, even exterior changes, are made in the name of educational improvement.

From Deficit to Development

What we can do in the classroom is limited, of course, by other factors. Students must be there to benefit from what happens in class. Teachers know firsthand that far too many young people of high school age are no longer even enrolled. Nationally, the drop-out rate in 1980 among the high school population aged 14 to 34 was 13 percent. It was higher among low-income and minority students. Nearly 1 out of 10 high schools had a drop-out rate of over 20 percent.[8]

Even when students stay in high school, we know that they do not always have access to the academic preparation they need. Many do not take enough of the right kinds of courses. In 1980, in almost half of all high schools, a majority of the students in each of those schools was enrolled in the "general" curriculum. Nationwide, only 38 percent of high school seniors had been in an academic program; another 36 percent had been in a general program; and 24 percent had followed a vocational/technical track. Only 39 percent of these seniors had enrolled for three or more years in history or social studies; only 33 percent had taken three or more

---

8. National Center for Education Statistics, *Digest of Education Statistics: 1982*, p. 68. Donald A. Rock, et al., "Factors Associated with Test Score Decline: Briefing Paper" (Princeton, New Jersey: Educational Testing Service, December 1984), p. 4.

years of mathematics; barely 22 percent had taken three or more years of science; and less than 8 percent of these students had studied Spanish, French, or German for three or more years.[9]

Better than anyone else, teachers know that, even when students are in high school and are enrolled in the needed academic courses, they must attend class regularly. Yet some school systems report daily absence rates as high as 20 percent. When 1 out of 5 students enrolled in a course is not actually there, it is difficult even to begin carrying out a sustained, coherent program of academic preparation.

As teachers we know that such problems cannot be solved solely by our efforts in the classroom. In a world of disrupted family and community structures; economic hardship; and rising teenage pregnancy, alcoholism, and suicide, it would be foolish to believe that attention to curriculum and instruction can remedy all the problems leading to students' leaving high school, taking the wrong courses, and missing classes. Nonetheless, what happens in the high school classroom—once students are there—is important in preparing students not only for further education but for life.

Moreover, as teachers, we also hope that what happens in the classroom at least can help students stick with their academic work. Students may be increasingly receptive to this view. In 1980 more than 70 percent of high school seniors wanted greater academic emphasis in their schools; this was true of students in all curricula. Mortimer Adler may have described a great opportunity:

> There is little joy in most of the learning they [students] are now compelled to do. Too much of it is make-believe, in which neither teacher nor pupil can take a lively interest. Without some joy in learning—a joy that arises from hard work well done and from the participation of one's mind in a common task—basic schooling cannot initiate the young into the life of learning, let alone give them the skill and the incentive to engage in it further.[10]

---

9. National Center for Education Statistics, *Digest of Education Statistics: 1982*, p. 70.

10. Mortimer J. Adler, *The Paideia Proposal: An Educational Manifesto* (New York: Macmillan Publishing Company, 1982), p. 32.

Genuine academic work can contribute to student motivation and persistence. Goodlad's study argues strongly that the widespread focus on the rote mechanics of a subject is a surefire way to distance students from it or to ensure that they do not comprehend all that they are capable of understanding. Students need to be encouraged to become inquiring, involved learners. It is worth trying to find more and better ways to engage them actively in the learning process, to build on their strengths and enthusiasms. Consequently, the approaches suggested in these books try to shift attention from chronicling what students do not know toward developing the full intellectual attainments of which they are capable and which they will need in college.

Dimensions for a Continuing Dialogue

This book and its five companions were prepared during 1984 and 1985 under the aegis of the College Board's Academic Advisory Committees. Although each committee focused on the particular issues facing its subject, the committees had common purposes and common approaches. Those purposes and approaches may help give shape to the discussion that this book and its companions hope to stimulate.

Each committee sought the assistance of distinguished writers and consultants. The committees considered suggestions made in the dialogues that preceded and contributed to *Academic Preparation for College* and called on guest colleagues for further suggestions and insights. Each committee tried to take account of the best available thinking and research but did not merely pass along the results of research or experience. Each deliberated about those findings and then tried to suggest approaches that had actually worked to achieve learning outcomes described in *Academic Preparation for College*. The suggestions in these books are based to a great extent on actual, successful high school programs.

These books focus not only on achieving the outcomes for a particular subject described in the Green Book but also on how study of that subject can develop the Basic Academic Competencies. The learning special to each subject has a central role to play in preparing students for successful work in college. That role ought not to be neglected in a rush to equip students with more general skills. It is learning in a subject that can engage a student's interest, activity, and commitment. Students do, after all, read about *something*, write about *something*, reason about *something*. We thought it important to suggest that developing the Basic Academic Competencies does not replace, but can result from, mastering the unique knowledge and skills of each Basic Academic Subject. Students, particularly hungry and undernourished ones, should not be asked to master the use of the fork, knife, and spoon without being served an appetizing, full, and nourishing meal.

In preparing the book for each subject, we also tried to keep in mind the connections among the Basic Academic Subjects. For example, the teaching of English and the other languages should build on students' natural linguistic appetite and development—and this lesson may apply to the teaching of other subjects as well. The teaching of history with emphasis on the full range of human experience, as approached through both social and global history, bears on the issue of broadening the "canon" of respected works in literature and the arts. The teaching of social studies, like the teaching of science, involves mathematics not only as a tool but as a mode of thought. There is much more to make explicit and to explore in such connections among the Basic Academic Subjects. Teachers may teach in separate departments, but students' thought is probably not divided in the same way.

Finally, the suggestions advanced here generally identify alternate ways of working toward the same outcomes. We wanted very much to avoid any hint that there is one and only one way to achieve the outcomes described in *Academic Preparation for College*. There are many good ways of achieving the desired results, each one good in its own way and in particular circumstances. By describing alternate approaches, we hope to encourage readers of this book to analyze and recombine alternatives and to create the most appropriate and effective approaches, given their own particular situations.

We think that this book and its five companion volumes can be useful to many people. Individual teachers may discover suggestions that will spur their own thought about what might be done in the classroom; small groups of teachers may find the book useful in reconsidering the science program in their high school. It also may provide a takeoff point for in-service sessions. Teachers in several subjects might use it and its companions to explore concerns, such as the Basic Academic Competencies, that range across the high school curriculum. Principals may find these volumes useful in refreshing the knowledge and understanding on which their own instructional leadership is based.

We also hope that these books will prove useful to committees of teachers and officials in local school districts and at the state level who are examining the high school curriculum established in their jurisdictions. Public officials whose decisions directly or indirectly affect the conditions under which teaching and learning occur may find in the books an instructive glimpse of the kinds of things that should be made possible in the classroom.

Colleges and universities may find in all six books occasion to consider not only how they are preparing future teachers, but also whether their own curricula will be suited to students receiving the kinds of preparation these books suggest. But our greatest hope is that this book and its companions will be used as reference points for dialogues between high school and college teachers. It was from such dialogues that *Academic Preparation for College* emerged. We believe that further discussions of this sort can provide a wellspring of insight and energy to move beyond the Green Book toward actually providing the knowledge and skills all students need to be successful in college.

We understand the limitations of the suggestions presented here. Concerning what happens in the classroom, many teachers, researchers, and professional associations can speak with far greater depth and detail than is possible in the pages that follow. This book aspires only to get that conversation going, particularly across the boundaries that usually divide those concerned about education, and especially as it concerns the students who often are least well served. Curriculum, teaching, and learning are far too central to be omitted from the discussion about improving education.

II. Preparation and Outcomes

Academic Preparation for College points out that all college-bound students "will need not only to know about science but also to understand the fundamentals of how to carry out scientific work." In the prologue, To Our Fellow Teachers of Science, we stressed that, as science teachers, we are concerned that students learn both the content and the processes of science. The structured body of knowledge that makes up the content of modern science is rich, elaborate, and absorbing. Indeed, for many high school students of science, it can be very nearly overwhelming. But that body of knowledge was produced by the work of scientists, and it continues to be revised and transformed by means of the processes of inquiry they employ. As students become more accomplished in carrying out these processes, they become able to acquire, comprehend, and retain more of the body of scientific knowledge. Consequently, the learning outcomes for the high school study of science listed in *Academic Preparation for College* give prominence to the scientific competencies and skills students will need.

This emphasis on learning how to do science is consistent with a long tradition. In 1886 Harvard College issued the earliest specific recommendations for preparing high school students in science for college work. One requirement for admissions credit in physics was ". . . a course of experiments in the subjects of mechanics, sound, light, heat, and electricity, not less than 40 in number, actually performed at school by the pupil." Included was a list of the 40 experiments. After performing them, the student was to write them up in a notebook and have them graded and certified by the high school teacher. Then the student was asked to appear, notebook in hand, for an on-campus laboratory performance test.

Two years after this list came out, Harvard issued another set of requirements, this time for admissions credit in laboratory chemistry. It included an elaborate list of 83 mostly quantitative experiments, 60 of which had to be performed and written up. In subsequent years the requirements for admissions credit in physiography, meteorology, physiology, zoology, and botany all included strong doses of laboratory and field work.

As soon as the physics list was issued, New England high schools on the Harvard pipeline scrambled to put in extra laboratory instruction; following this lead, other schools also began emphasizing laboratory work. Recitation classes sometimes were dropped entirely to let the students spend their time doing experiments.

This extreme emphasis on laboratory work did not last. It was not practical; teachers complained that their courses had become too narrow and too quantitative. By 1912 all laboratory science requirements for Harvard admissions credits had been abandoned. Nevertheless, notions of what constitutes an adequate high school science course were changed forever. Though Harvard's lists can be faulted, the importance to precollegiate study of learning actually to "do" science continues to be widely recognized.

Since the days of the Harvard lists, many others have drawn up specifications for science instruction in secondary school, though substantiation for them is often hard to come by. Recently, for example, notable commentators in education, industry, and government have voiced the opinion that the nation's high school graduates need to become more "scientifically literate." One related set of recommendations was issued in 1983 by the National Science Board Commission on Precollege Education in Mathematics, Science, and Technology (see footnote 2, Chapter 3). The ultimate goal of these recommendations is to produce scientifically and technologically literate citizens. But is that goal attainable? The question cannot be answered with a resounding yes. A major difficulty is determining what the concept of scientific literacy means in practice. Although the idea has been discussed for decades, there is still little agreement about what scientifically literate citizens understand, which skills they possess, and how they behave. Even less clear is what is meant by the newer idea of technological literacy. Thus there is no easy way to determine which education outcomes will help students attain this goal.

We believe that the case is different for the recommendations about precollege science education outlined in *Academic Preparation for College*. Attainment of their goal, success in college, can readily be measured by means of college grades. Moreover, these outcomes summarize the experience and judgment of hundreds of college and high school teachers about what actually contributes to success in college. Further, the recommendations are firmly supported by a body of research that goes back to the late 1930s. For example, one finding, repeatedly replicated, is that mathematical skills are critical to success in college courses in the physical sciences and engineering. Another replicated finding is that students familiar with the processes of scientific inquiry tend to earn higher grades in college science courses for nonmajors. It has also been shown that, surprisingly, students who have taken a particular high school science course—chemistry, for example—do not generally achieve better in introductory college courses in the same science than do students who have not taken the high school course. In preparing for college, then, mastering science skills and understanding fundamental concepts are more useful than completing a particular high school science course. Findings like these indicate that the learning outcomes described in the Green Book provide a plausible as well as verifiable basis for planning high school science instruction.

A Framework for the Outcomes

The aim of both scientists and science students is to build up reliable knowledge and understanding of the natural world. Understanding in the sciences comes in several varieties and involves a range of activities, from observation of phenomena to symbolic representations of ideas and relationships. The varieties of understanding are interconnected both in the development of each science field and in the development of students' learning.

The earliest scientists were engaged primarily in observation and description, and much of the knowledge amassed by contemporary scientists is also *descriptive:* the characteristics used to classify animal and plant species, the properties of chemical substances, the strata of geologic formations. Students' understanding of science develops from the same descriptive base. For example, when a clear, sour liquid is poured on a certain light-gray rock, a froth of bubbles appears where the liquid contacts the rock. When an observation has been accurately and lucidly described, new questions usually occur to students, as to practicing scientists. Do bubbles form when a different sour liquid is poured on this rock, or is the effect produced only by this particular liquid? If this liquid is poured on several types of rock, what else is there in common? Further observations can answer such questions and yield a wealth of descriptive information. Such information is essential for understanding the natural world.

Qualitative understanding seeks to explain what is observed. One type of qualitative explanation concerns inherent qualities. Centuries ago Aristotle suggested that matter has four such qualities: heat, cold, moisture, and dryness. Today we continue to ascribe certain qualities to matter to explain the characteristics and behaviors we have observed. For example, to explain our observation that white, solid crystals of sodium chloride disappear when they are stirred with water, we talk about the solubility of sodium chloride. Another type of qualitative explanation is comparative: we speak of a substance being heavier, less soluble, or brighter. This type of qualitative understanding verges on the quantitative, but it is often used even when numerical measures are available (for example, volume, weight, speed, energy). Not only students, but research scientists in both physical and biological fields frequently use qualitative reasoning.

Quantitative understanding is characterized by measurements and mathematical methods. For example, quantities can be compared in terms of amounts expressed on a numerical scale: a certain white mineral has a density of 3.7 g/cm^3 while a certain green mineral's density is 2.8 g/cm^3. To explain phenomena and to reason about observations, there is an emphasis on identifying variables that increase and decrease in numerical value. Problems call for numerical solutions. To illustrate, in the synthesis of ammonia by the Haber process, how does doubling the external pressure affect the quantity of ammonia produced?

Symbolic understanding is the most abstract, as it is characterized by formulas, equations, and notations. The previous illustration of descriptive understanding involving a sour liquid poured on a light-gray rock can be put this way:

Hydrochloric acid + calcium carbonate
= carbon dioxide gas + water + calcium chloride solution

Put another way, the chemical reaction that occurs can be represented as follows:

$$2H^+ (aq) + CaCO_3 (s) = CO_2 (g) + H_2O (l) + Ca^{2+} (aq)$$

The symbols and conventions in this equation tell us that 2 moles of hydrochloric acid react with 1 mole of calcium carbonate to yield 1 mole of carbon dioxide gas, which is released as a gas, 1 mole of water, and 1 mole of calcium ions. (The chloride ions from the hydrochloric acid do not appear in the chemical equation because they do not take part in the reaction that occurs. After the reaction is completed—that is, after enough hydrochloric acid has been added to use up all the calcium carbonate—evaporation of the resulting solution will yield 1 mole of calcium chloride.)

The symbols also convey information concerning the chemical elements contained in each of the five substances and the atomic constituents of their molecules. For instance, the equation's second substance, calcium carbonate, is a chemical compound that contains the elements calcium, carbon, and oxygen; the constituents of calcium carbonate in their smallest ratio are one calcium atom, one carbon atom, and three oxygen atoms.

The various concepts, definitions, images, and operations associated with the symbols and conventions shown in this equation extend, of course, much further. For example, the chemical equation also conveys the concept of conservation of mass in a chemical reaction. A similar wealth of meaning is associated with most abstract symbols used in science. In symbolic understanding, students are expected to grasp such associated meanings, though they are rarely made explicit. For this reason, many students find symbolic understanding quite challenging.

In qualitative, quantitative, and symbolic understanding, scientists develop conceptual schemes to account for observations and relationships. These conceptual schemes, or scientific theories, may be quite simple or highly sophisticated. Major conceptual schemes, such as the theory of evolution, the kinetic-molecular theory, and the atomic theory, seek to provide satisfying explanations for a very broad range of phenomena and principles.

In this book we suggest that the different varieties of scientific understanding require different instructional strategies in the laboratory and the field; successful hands-on experience can both exemplify the processes of scientific inquiry and help students achieve proficiency in the different varieties of scientific understanding. Consequently we use the framework of descriptive, qualitative, quantitative, and symbolic varieties of scientific understanding as the context for the instructional strategies discussed in Chapter 4 and for the following elaboration of the specific science learning outcomes sketched in the Green Book.

Academic Preparation in College emphasizes not only the laboratory and field work that is integral to science but also the mathematical skills that are essential to much of quantitative and symbolic understanding. In calling attention to the importance of mathematical skills in precollegiate science education, we do not mean to deemphasize descriptive and qualitative understanding. Quite the reverse. We have suggested the important role of these two varieties of understanding in the work of contemporary scientists and in the historical development of the sciences. They are no less important in the development of students' learning. Descriptive and qualitative understanding are the base on which conceptual schemes rest, the needed precursors to quantitative and symbolic understanding. If students lack this firm grounding, the quantitative and symbolic can become a rootless blur or a rote exercise in manipulating meaningless numbers. *Academic Preparation for College* calls attention to mathematical skills because too many students are stopped short of such needed preparation and because many high schools must give further consideration to the means of providing such skills to more students. But descriptive work and qualitative work in the sciences are important in their own right and fundamental to developing quantitative and symbolic understanding. Indeed, this foundation should be prepared not only during but even before the high school years.

Laboratory and Mathematical Skills

This section illustrates and elaborates on most of the science learning outcomes listed in *Academic Preparation for College*. The first division in that listing concerns laboratory and field work; the second concerns mathematical skills, most of which the student brings to bear on data and results obtained in the laboratory or the field. Consequently, the outcomes are presented here as a related and reordered set of specific activities. Appendix A presents those outcomes as they were listed in *Academic Preparation for College* and indicates how they have been reordered.

Students come to the study of science with many commonsense beliefs about the natural world. They can also bring a sense of curiosity or wonder about the workings of that world. Their curiosity can be engaged and focused, their beliefs refined or revised as they learn to employ scientific processes. Although the work of scientists is sometimes characterized by sudden leaps and flashes of insight, such jumps typically spring from disciplined, expert intelligence. They involve an implicit understanding of the processes of science. By making the components of these processes explicit, we do not mean to suggest that high school science instruction need be sluggish or halting. Rather, we believe instruction can become increasingly effective as teachers recognize these components and provide students opportunity to master them as part of the whole process of doing science.

Gathering Scientific Information

- *Outcome A. The skills to gather scientific information through laboratory, field, and library work.* This outcome can be elaborated as follows:

A.1 Observing objects and phenomena.

A.2 Describing observations using appropriate language.

A.3 Selecting appropriate measuring instruments.

A.4 Measuring objects and changes.

A.5 Processing observational and experimental data.

A.6 Developing skills in using common laboratory and field equipment.

A.7 Carrying out common laboratory techniques with care and safety.

To illustrate, we consider examples relating to simple heat phenomena. A student might be watching an ice cube in a glass of water in a warm room or noting changes of the water in a beaker being heated on a hot plate (A.1). Many different things can be observed in a few minutes and then communicated orally or in writing (A.2). These two behaviors are the crux of descriptive understanding. In describing observations, the student should place the emphasis on effective communication rather than the form of the language. The latter can vary widely. "The outside of the glass got wet" is as appropriate for eighth- or ninth-grade students as "Moisture accumulated on the glass's outer surface" is for older students. Understanding in science is not merely a matter of using the right words.

A student's observations can go beyond description and simple counting to the use of an instrument to measure objects and changes (A.4). The initial temperature of the water in the beaker may be measured with a thermometer and found to be 22°C. As the water in the beaker is heated, the temperature may be found to change from 22°C to 24°C after one minute, to 27°C at the end of the second minute, and to 30°C at the end of the third minute. After several more minutes, when the reading on the thermometer reaches 100°C, the temperature does not go up, despite continued heating. To obtain such data, the student must have selected the appropriate measuring instrument (A.3). The instrument must be capable of measuring the desired quantity and must be operative over the range of the quantity to be measured. A stopwatch is not the appropriate instrument for measuring the temperature of water in a beaker; a mercury-in-glass thermometer is not appropriate for measuring the temperature of the melt in a blast furnace.

Students obtain data in the form of recorded observations and measurements, which must usually be processed, that is, mathematically manipulated and adjusted to yield values for the quantities under study (A.5). In a typical calorimetric experiment to determine the amount of heat gained by a sample of lead, the measurements recorded are the sample's mass, its initial temperature, and its final temperature. Processing these data includes subtracting the initial from the final temperature and multiplying the difference by the sample's mass and by the specific heat of lead to yield the number of calories gained. In volumetric experiments with gases, processing recorded data includes adjusting the actual measurements in volume to standard temperature and pressure (STP) by using the recorded measurements of atmospheric pressure and room temperature.

This outcome also implies that students need to develop skills in using common laboratory and field equipment (A.6)—for example, lighting and regulating the flame of a Bunsen burner. Other common equipment that students should learn to manipulate includes the balance, microscope, ruler, tree corer, rain gauge, and chemical glassware. Beyond these manual and coordinating skills, students must learn to carry out common laboratory techniques with care and safety (A.7). A sequence of manipulations must be tailored to fit a defined end. Such techniques as collecting a sample of gas insoluble in water, preparing thin tissue sections for microscopic examination, or dissecting an animal specimen must be applied carefully, so that useful results can be obtained. Finally, it *is* necessary to point out that preventing injury to either the equipment or the experimenter requires constant attention to safety.

Of the components of Outcome A, observing objects and phenomena (A.1) and describing observations using appropriate language (A.2) contribute to either descriptive or qualitative understanding. Measuring objects and changes (A.4) relates to both qualitative and quantitative understanding. Selecting appropriate measuring instruments (A.3) and processing observational and experimental data (A.5) both promote quantitative understanding. The final two components, developing skills in using equipment (A.6) and carrying out laboratory techniques with care and safety (A.7), can contribute to descriptive, qualitative, or quantitative understanding.

Overall, this outcome has to do with gathering scientific information. Although the illustrations given here are drawn from laboratory work, much the same kinds of things might be said in connection with field work. Moreover, this is the context in which we locate science students' work in the library. Such work should involve the gathering of scientific information produced by previous investigations, which students can use for further inquiry and analysis. Like laboratory and field work, library work should provide students with the basis for further questioning, not with ready-made answers.

Approaching Scientific Questions Experimentally

■ *Outcome B. Sufficient familiarity with laboratory and field work to ask appropriate scientific questions and to recognize what is involved in experimental approaches to the solutions of such questions.* In this outcome the following set of behaviors is involved:

B.1 Recognizing a problem.
B.2 Formulating a working hypothesis.
B.3 Selecting suitable tests of a hypothesis.
B.4 Designing appropriate procedures for performing experimental tests.

To illustrate these behaviors, let us look at them in the context of another illustration involving heat. As part of a class exercise, a student has heated a beaker of water to 80°C on a hot plate. Leaving the thermometer in the water, the student removes the beaker from the hot plate and places it on her desk. After five minutes, the thermometer reads 72°C. The student recognizes a problem. She wishes to investigate heat phenomena in liquids, but this will be difficult if she has to contend with apparently spontaneous losses of heat. The problem is how to minimize such heat losses. Obviously, the container must be covered, but what materials should be used for the containers to hold the liquid samples? Is heat loss through the walls of a container the same for all materials?

Recognizing a problem (B.1) may thus pass through several stages: from an awareness of the problem area to the identification of a specific problem that can be investigated experimentally. Asking if heat loss is the same through all materials is an example of the latter. It may lead to formulating a working hypothesis (B.2) to give direction to the investigation. For example, heat is lost more readily through the walls of containers made of some materials than through the walls of containers made of other materials. Another hypothesis may be that the amount of heat lost depends on the thickness of the walls of the container and not on the container's composition. Both hypotheses involve quantitative understanding, but hypotheses are possible at the qualitative or descriptive levels as well.

Formulating a working hypothesis, particularly with respect to such a simple case, may seem to be a routine matter to those who already have assimilated science's understanding of such situations. For a young high school student, however, formulating a hypothesis—if properly handled—can be an opportunity to surface (and subsequently put to a test) some already held commonsense beliefs about the phenomenon in question. The expected answers are by no means the only hypotheses that seem plausible to young people.

Selecting suitable tests of a hypothesis (B.3) involves choosing an approach that can logically verify the hypothesis. The level of science understanding here corresponds to that of the hypothesis to be tested. This component is a matter of valid strategy, not yet of constructing or manipulating apparatus. For example, a valid test of the hypothesis that the heat lost from a container depends on the thickness of its walls and not on its composition would require selecting a twofold experimental approach: first, measuring heat losses in containers made of the same material but with different wall thicknesses; second, measuring heat losses in containers with the same wall thickness but made of different materials. A suitable test of the first hypothesis, that heat is lost more readily through the walls of containers made of some materials than through the walls of containers made of other materials, is more straightforward. The student simply would have to decide to measure heat losses in containers made of different materials, but whose walls had the same thickness. Again with this component, something that may seem routine or automatic to the expert can be of crucial importance to the student. Laboratory manipulations can be pointless and isolated from their context—mere "cookbook chemistry"—if students have not already determined in their own minds how those manipulations bear on the point at issue, the hypothesis.

Finally, before testing her hypothesis, the student has to devise appropriate procedures (B.4). A procedure for measuring heat losses in containers made of different materials would be to (1) obtain containers of exactly the same size, shape, and wall thickness, but of different materials; (2) fill each container to the same level with boiling water; (3) stir the water with a glass rod and record the water temperature with a thermometer; (4) continue stirring and record the water temperature every 60 seconds for a period of 30 minutes. In this illustration the equipment and procedures are simple, but in many student experiments they may be fairly complex and elaborate.

Organizing and Communicating Results

■ *Outcome C. The ability to organize and communicate the results obtained by observation and experimentation. The ability to interpret data presented in tabular and graphic form.* After gathering information and processing their data, students must organize the processed data and apply their mathematical skills to analyze them. This outcome consists of:

C.1 Organizing data and observations.
C.2 Presenting data in the form of functional relationships.
C.3 Extrapolating functional relationships beyond actual observations, when warranted, and interpolating between observed points.
C.4 Interpreting data and observations.

Students need to learn to organize data and observations (C.1) in tables or charts that are easily readable and follow the conventions of the appropriate scientific field. For example, when numerical data are displayed in a table, the units for all measurements should be included in the headings and the proper number of significant figures should be used.

The next two components deal with the student's preparation and use of graphs. For example, suppose that in measuring the volume of a sample of air at different temperatures but under constant pressure, a student finds that the volume of the sample was 18.7 cc at a temperature of 100°C (or 373 K), 14.6 cc at 20°C (or 293 K), 13.7 cc at 0°C (or 273 K), and 11.6 cc at −40°C (or 233 K). To present these data in the form of a functional relationship (C.2), the student plots the data points on graph paper with absolute temperature (the Kelvin scale) on one axis and volume on the other.

Since the points lie along a single straight line passing through the origin, the graph shows a functional relationship: the volume of a sample of air is directly proportional to absolute temperature when the pressure is held constant. Extrapolating, when warranted, of functional relationships beyond the actual observations and interpolating between the observed points (C.3) can also be done from a graph. In the above illustration, observations were made at 20°C and at 0°C, but the volume of air at 10°C (283 K) was not measured. Interpolation reveals the volume at 283 K to be 14.2 cc. Extrapolating beyond the observed temperatures would show the volume of the air to be 21.3 cc at 425 K and 8.6 cc at 174 K. These steps are warranted because no intervening conditions alter the functional relationship between temperature and volume of air. An extrapolation to 73 K would not be warranted, of course, because the air would have changed from a gas to a liquid and the temperature-volume relationship does not take this intervening condition into account.

Finally, the student begins to analyze the results of an experiment by interpreting experimental data and observations (C.4). When the data are presented in a graph, interpretation involves formulating a discrete concept of what the experimental results signify. It also includes formulating a conception of the trends or functional relationships and translating this into equivalent verbal or symbolic form. For example, consider an experiment in which the volume of a sample of oxygen gas was measured under different external pressures and at constant temperature. A student might interpret the graph of the results by saying that the volume of oxygen is inversely proportional to the external pressure at constant temperature, or, in symbols, $PV = k$ where k is a constant for a constant temperature.

The components of Outcome C could relate to several varieties of science understanding. Organizing data and observations (C.1) could involve descriptive, qualitative, or quantitative understanding. Presenting data in the form of functional relationships (C.2) and extrapolating functional relationships beyond actual observations and interpolating between observed points (C.3) are clearly quantitative. Finally, interpreting data and observations (C.4) could involve qualitative or quantitative understanding.

Drawing Conclusions

■ *Outcome D. The ability to draw conclusions or make inferences from data, observation, and experimentation, and to apply mathematical relationships to scientific problems.*

After a hypothesis has been tested and the data have been collected, processed, organized, and interpreted, the student needs to determine whether the findings verify the hypothesis. In actual practice, the relation of students' thought to a hypothesis can be a tricky matter. On the one hand, we have seen that such preliminary formulations can play a vital role in bringing out already held commonsense beliefs and in giving direction and shape to an investigation. On the other hand, mechanically restricting students' thought to a single explanatory possibility can stifle the natural curiosity by which they can recognize other variables and ultimately come upon valid conclusions. In any case, drawing valid conclusions involves the same kind of thought whether the data are quantitative, qualitative, or descriptive. This process of confronting a hypothesis with findings involves not quantitative but verbal reasoning skills.

Students can go beyond conclusions about particular hypotheses to generalizing findings. To illustrate, an inquiry into how the volume of air changes at different temperatures found that, at constant pressure, the volume of a sample of air increases linearly as its absolute temperature increases. Students naturally will ask if this finding represents a general principle applicable to all samples of air. Moreover, they may wonder if this is an empirical law covering all gases, not only air. In answering these questions, students generalize to empirical laws or principles warranted by the relationships found. They consider the results of experiments with other samples of air and similar inquiries using different gases. If the original findings are corroborated, students are justified in formulating an empirical generalization: at constant pressure, the volume of a gas is directly proportional to its absolute temperature. Here students are making comparisons of the results of several inquiries and deriving from all the available evidence an abstract relation covering a range of related phenomena. The generalization synthesizes the various results in a compact form.

When students evaluate hypotheses in the light of data or formulate generalizations warranted by multiple findings, they employ their verbal reasoning skills. This is true both when students reason about qualitative relationships and even in instances when they are reasoning about mathematical relationships. Similarly, students must employ their verbal reasoning skills when they solve science problems, and this holds true for solving both qualitative and quantitative problems. Because solving quantitative problems requires students to employ reasoning skills and to apply their knowledge of science and mathematical relationships, this is an effective way to develop and assess students' understanding.

In short, Outcome D can involve:

D.1 Evaluating a hypothesis in the light of observations and experimental data.

D.2 Formulating appropriate generalizations, that is, empirical laws or principles warranted by the relationships found.

D.3 Applying mathematical relationships in solving science problems.

Recognizing the Role of Observation and Experimentation in Theories

- *Outcome E. The ability to recognize the role of observation and experimentation in the development of scientific theories.*

Comprehensive and well-tested theories give modern science much of its vast range and power of explanation. It is precisely this range and power, however, that makes understanding how theory is based on observation and experimentation among the most problematic of science learning outcomes. It is difficult for high school students to pursue the processes of scientific thought all the way to the stage of building and elaborating theories. Teachers end up having to describe the relation of phenomena, principles, and laws to broader theories. Nonetheless, recognizing this relationship is crucial to learning science. Absent such recognition, scientific theories can be mistaken for groundless assertions—interchangeable "positions"—one as acceptable as the next. Consequently, it is worth trying to identify in this outcome things that students might come to recognize and understand by means—on some scale, at least—

of their own intellectual activity. Overall, this outcome could involve the following components:

E.1 Recognizing the need for a theory to relate different phenomena and empirical laws or principles.

E.2 Formulating a theory to accommodate known phenomena and principles.

E.3 Specifying the phenomena and principles that are satisfied or explained by a theory.

E.4 Deducing new hypotheses from a theory to direct observations and experiments for testing it.

E.5 Interpreting and evaluating the results of the experiments to test a theory.

E.6 Formulating, when warranted by new observations or interpretations, a revised, refined, or extended theory.

Students could come to recognize the need for a theory to relate different phenomena and empirical laws or principles (E.1) by following relevant case studies. For example, during the nineteenth century many chemists would not give serious consideration to atomic theory. They held that the only proper concern of chemistry was visible properties and changes. Their science solely involved various chemical laws and principles generalized from their laboratory experiences. Today, like all sciences, chemistry employs not only empirical laws but also theories in order to organize known phenomena. With a teacher's help, students could come to see how atomic theory explains the law of definite composition and the law of multiple proportions and how it has suggested further inquiries. Students can come to recognize that scientific theory serves three major functions. First, a theory correlates or ties together in a consistent, rational manner the various phenomena and generalizations it covers. Second, a theory accounts for or explains these observations and generalizations. Finally, a theory is heuristic; it suggests new hypotheses, problems, and experiments that will give direction to further inquiries.

In the context of a theory-building exercise devised by their teacher, students might attain a more active understanding of the role of observation and experimentation in the development of scientific theories. Obviously, the average high school student is in no position to work at the frontiers of current scientific theory. A teacher, however, might draw out and make explicit the common-sense beliefs students already hold about some topic. Such an "everyday theory" could provide the basis for an extensive elaboration of student thought. Formulating a theory to accommodate known phenomena and principles (E.2) would involve a broad, general statement about the phenomena in an area of inquiry—a statement consisting of a small set of postulates. For example, even after some time spent investigating heat phenomena, students might believe that the various observations and generalizations could be explained by thinking of heat as a fluid substance. This theory could assume the following set of postulates:

1. Heat is a colorless, odorless, invisible fluid substance.
2. Heat fluid occupies space and has mass, like other substances, but it has a very small mass.
3. Heat fluid flows spontaneously from regions of high concentration to regions of low concentration (from hot objects to cooler objects).
4. Heat fluid is always associated with matter, and it increases disorder in the arrangement of particles of matter.
5. Heat fluid readily enters some gases, liquids, and solids, but it does not readily enter other gases, liquids, and solids.
6. When matter changes its state from solid to liquid or from liquid to gas, it absorbs heat fluid, and when matter changes its state from gas to liquid or from liquid to solid, it releases heat fluid.

What is actually a widely held "everyday theory" of heat could then be tried out by using it to account for or explain specific heat phenomena and principles (E.3). Unlike evaluating hypotheses by the use of observational evidence (D.1), here a student analyzes the relationship of a theory to both generalized evidence—empirical laws and principles—and discrete observations. For example: metals are good conductors of heat, but plastics are not—explained by postulate 5; when water at 60°C is added to water at 20°C, the resulting temperature of the water mixture is greater than 20°C—explained by postulate 3; the volume of a given quantity of any solid, liquid, or gas increases when it is heated—explained by postulates 2, 3, and 4; additional heating is required to change water at 100°C to steam at 100°C—explained by postulate 6; at constant pressure, the volume of a gas is directly proportional to its absolute temperature—explained by postulates 2 and 4. The more observations and principles a student can encompass by the theory, the more successful it is in fulfilling its correlative and explanatory function.

The heuristic function of a theory involves deducing new hypotheses to direct observations and experiments (E.4). First, a student might reason from, and in terms of, the theory to certain deductions or hypotheses. Then the student would propose a plan of experiments and observations. Here the proposed plan of inquiry serves to test not only the hypothesis, but also the theory behind the hypothesis. To illustrate, postulate 2 states that heat fluid, like other substances, has mass, though its mass is very small. Postulate 3 asserts that a hot object contains more heat fluid than does a cold object. A student might deduce the hypothesis that an object has a greater mass when it is hot than when it is cold, though the comparison would have to be made over a large temperature difference.

Another student might deduce from postulate 5—heat fluid readily enters some substances but not others—that a characteristic of different metals is their differing capacities to increase their temperature when the same amount of heat is available. The hypothesis would be that each kind of metal has a "specific heat" that can be used to identify it. For either of these hypotheses the students would next propose tests by means of appropriate experiments and observations. Such investigations would return to the processes described under Outcomes A through D, thus indicating the heuristic function of the theory.

Interpreting and evaluating the results of the experiments to test a theory (E.5) would include analyzing not only the relationship between the empirical evidence obtained and the hypothesis tested, but also the relationship between the empirical evidence and the theory from which the hypothesis was deduced. In addition, the theory itself calls for evaluation: judgments must be made about its consistency, precision, and persuasiveness. Here students might join in discussions and even arguments, since controversy is not unusual among scientists when evaluating competing theories.

Suppose a student has results from experiments with many different metals showing that the "specific heat" of every metal tested differs from that of every other metal. These results confirm his hypothesis that each kind of metal has a "specific heat" that can be used to identify it, and give him increased confidence in the heat fluid theory from which he deduced the hypothesis.

Another student, however, has the results of many careful experiments repeatedly carried out to test the hypothesis that an object has a greater mass when it is hot than when it is cold. In no experiment was an increase detected in the mass of a metal when its temperature was raised as much as 200°C.[1] These results indicate that this student's hypothesis is not correct, and the failure to confirm it suggests that postulate 2 of the heat fluid theory—heat fluid has mass—is not correct. The student may now question the entire theory that conceives of heat as a fluid substance. If heat fluid has no mass, this student may say, it is inconsistent to assume that heat is a substance, since no other substance without mass is known.

The first student, however—having gained confidence in the heat fluid theory—could answer that the mass of heat fluid may be much smaller than originally anticipated, so small that the addition of a temperature increase of only 200°C cannot be detected with the instruments used. A lively discussion might ensue, as each student marshals evidence, reasoned arguments, and judgments to interpret the results of experiments and evaluate the theory.

At some juncture a revised, refined, or extended theory may have to be formulated, because it is warranted by new observations or interpretations (E.6). The thought processes here are not essentially different from those required for the original formulation of a theory (E.2), but the reformulation must take into account the new experiences and ideas developed since then. In typical instructional situations in schools, many observations and generalizations about heat would satisfactorily be correlated and explained by the original heat fluid theory, and some hypotheses deduced from it would be confirmed by experiments. Other observations of heat phenomena and some derived hypotheses that were found to be incorrect would suggest that the heat fluid theory was inadequate. A new formulation must try to incorporate all this information and remedy the

---

1. For such experiments it is better to use a spring balance rather than an equal-arm balance because the latter may reflect change in the buoyant force of air.

defects of the original theory without sacrificing its positive features. Postulates may be changed or added to the old heat fluid theory. The theory may be revised entirely, for instance, by conceiving of heat as caused by the motion of the particles in a substance. The new theory, of course, will be subject to the same process of testing and revision. By working in such a defined domain, students may be able to acquire and display a more active understanding of the role of observation and experimentation in the development of scientific theories. In any case, a teacher's exposition of that role might follow the same sequence.

Fundamental Concepts

- *Outcome F. Understanding in some depth of the unifying concepts of the life and physical sciences.*

Here we proceed to address the content of science directly. In particular we focus on the third division of the science learning outcomes outlined in *Academic Preparation for College:* fundamental concepts. What working scientists find most satisfying about a successful theory is that it relates and explains a whole range of phenomena in a concise yet comprehensive way. They can point to the handful of verbal or mathematical statements that express the theory's powerful ideas—ideas that explain a significant segment of the natural world. They are pleased that the ideas in the newly developed theory promote a deeper understanding of the theory's domain and have more interconnections with related ideas than do previous explanations. Scientists in various fields have developed certain theories whose ideas have a very large scope. These ideas tie together and help explain so much of a science's domain that they can be thought of as fundamental.

This outcome statement stresses students' acquisition of knowledge about the pervasive themes that integrate large portions of the natural sciences and the major ideas that constitute important science theories. Students' understanding of such fundamental concepts, together with the related facts and principles, is an irreplaceable component of the understanding of science. The distinction between the content and the processes of science should not be carried too far, into an absolute separation or opposition. After all, under the preceding outcomes, which focus on the processes of science, students acquire knowledge of phenomena, of empirical generalizations, and finally of connections among them by means of theory. With respect to Outcome F we want to make the complementary point. What *Academic Preparation for College* means by "unifying concepts" and understanding them "in some depth" is that such ideas are connected to the other outcomes we have just discussed. The proper indication of how well students understand such ideas is not how elegant or elaborate a paraphrase of some term they can provide. The real test is the number and kinds of connections students can show between a theory and its postulates, various empirical laws and principles, and actual observable phenomena. Consequently, this last outcome could not be fulfilled by a general science course heaping up a multitude of terms and definitions.

The fundamental concepts of science can be unifying in a curricular sense as well, overcoming the fragmentation of experience in which students feel pelted by seemingly random, unconnected facts, formulas, and terminology. Many science teachers have devised effective ways to use fundamental concepts as organizing themes for their courses. Several major projects have undertaken this enterprise on a larger scale, notably Project Synthesis in 1978 and the Biological Sciences Curriculum Study of the 1960s. With respect to such efforts we conclude this chapter's exposition of needed learning in the processes and the content of science by emphasizing that this outcome has two interrelated components:

F.1 Understanding the unifying concepts of the sciences.
F.2 Understanding the nature of scientific inquiry.

III. The Curriculum

We want to contribute some relatively modest and practical suggestions to the discussion of high school curriculum in the natural sciences. That discussion can become extraordinarily complex, involving many different voices and perspectives. John Goodlad observed that in any given school there are actually five different curricula going on at once.[1]

1. The Ideal Curriculum (what scholars believe should be taught).
2. The Formal Curriculum (what some monitoring agency, such as the state or local district, has prescribed).
3. The Perceived Curriculum (what teachers believe they are teaching in response to student needs).
4. The Operational Curriculum (what an outside observer sees being taught in the classroom).
5. The Experiential Curriculum (what the students believe they are learning).

These different curricula are not isolated from one another. They are all part of the general discussion. In fact, a single individual might speak from the point of view of all five during a single meeting. In the end, however, the teachers must work together to make practical, classroom sense of curriculum. In sorting things out, it may be useful to refer to the following grid:

Ideal   Findings from current research in the teaching of science.

Formal   State and local mandates concerning knowledge and skills in science.

Perceived   Lists of the greatest strengths and weaknesses of students; lists of the most successful and least successful teaching attempts.

---

1. John Goodlad, *A Place Called School* (New York: McGraw-Hill, 1984).

Operational   What others have noted in evaluation reports, such as accrediting agency reports and reports from local supervisors.

Experiential   What students say in formal or informal course evaluations.

Such a means of informal analysis can help locate comments and arrange priorities within a more complete view. It may conserve time by framing the subject, suggesting a focus, or charting the ground to be covered. Often in curriculum discussions it is worthwhile to determine just what is being said and how it relates to the point at issue.

Criteria for Science Curriculum Selection

We believe that what is ultimately at issue in a discussion of curriculum is whether a proposed plan of teacher action will lead to the desired student learning. Without belaboring the point that teaching science can be seen as an object of empirical inquiry, it is relevant to approach possible curricula as hypotheses. Although the rapid expansion and frequent transformation of the body of scientific knowledge make the selection of topics an important matter, a science curriculum is not simply an inventory of "the most important" scientific theories, concepts, and facts. Still less is a science curriculum a "Missouri Compromise" among the interests of various individuals or groups, or a correlation of chapters or sections in a textbook to weeks and days in the school year. We see the science curriculum as a plan of action adopted so as to obtain desired results. The ultimate test of such a hypothesis is whether or not students do, in fact, learn what is intended. Initially, however, a proposed curriculum should be selected on the basis of its fit with the intended learning outcomes. Consistent with the aim of obtaining the learning outcomes described in Chapter 2 for as many students as possible, we suggest four criteria for use in selecting a science curriculum.

1. The curriculum should provide students opportunity to develop descriptive, qualitative, quantitative, and symbolic understanding of science.

In suggesting a framework for the outcomes, we noted that several varieties of understanding, ranging from the descriptive through the symbolic, characterize the natural sciences. It follows that a science curriculum should provide students at some time with the opportunity to work at all levels at which understanding is developed in each science discipline. Students should not be misled or impoverished by an incomplete version of the science they study.

The life sciences, for instance, do not just involve descriptions of living forms and phenomena, although the observations and classifications produced by descriptive natural history are very important. The life sciences also depend on exact measurements, numerical data, and quantitative comparisons. Abstract symbols—for example, $aaBb \times AAbb$—are frequently used to represent concepts and relationships. Similarly, physics is not properly presented as solely and strictly a quantitative and symbolic science, though these forms of representation play a great role. Physicists' own reflections indicate that, in large part, they think qualitatively, not quantitatively. Ignoring qualitative and descriptive understanding in physics is just as negligent as ignoring the quantitative and the symbolic in biology.

The curriculum should give students a view of the full range of each science domain they study. It should represent both the phenomena investigated and the large ideas developed to hold the field together, both qualitative distinctions and quantitative formulations, both the field's basic concepts and categories and the scientists' underlying assumptions and commitments. Neglecting some of these dimensions not only distorts the science in question; it limits the range of understanding that students can develop.

2. The curriculum should provide students opportunity to develop all the desired learning outcomes they can achieve.

Some of the outcome components described in Chapter 2 are relatively simple; some are quite sophisticated. None is likely to be achieved by students unless schools and teachers have a clear plan for instructional sequences to develop and practice them. Every science course needs well-planned sequences whose aims are the development of specific student skills and firm subject-matter understanding at identified levels.

Sufficient time must be allotted within each science course so that the varied students in the class, who begin at different levels of knowledge and possess different levels of skills, can complete all the instructional sequences for the course. We recall the emphasis placed by the noted educational theorists John Carroll and Benjamin Bloom on time as a major variable in determining students' successful learning. They may have underestimated the time needed for students to develop understanding, or they may have been too simplistic in viewing knowledge and skill acquisition as chiefly cumulative processes, but they did give us a fundamental insight. Most students are capable of attaining content mastery if they are provided enough time and appropriate instruction.

Allotting sufficient instructional time for students to develop targeted skills and specific understanding is much more important than "covering" unrealistic quantities of content. The content for any course should be sensibly limited so that the needed instructional time can be provided. This is one important reason that building a science curriculum cannot be approached simply as a matter of identifying important topics. In Chapter 6 we return to this question of selecting—and reducing the number of—topics in the science curriculum. For the moment we note that if the content for a given course is deliberately made to border on that of preceding and following courses in a sequence, the urge to "cover" everything may be reduced.

Science courses should build continuously toward students' development of sophisticated behaviors and understanding of content at multiple levels. Sequencing across courses is particularly important if instruction in a subsequent course assumes that students have certain skills (for example, reading a thermometer or plotting data on a graph) and understand certain ideas (for example, adaptation or osmosis). The development of a sophisticated skill should not lie fallow for a whole year. For example, suppose that students' interpretation of data or evaluation of experimental hypotheses reaches a certain stage in a grade 9 course. It is unwise to make no provision in the entire grade 10 course for further development or practice of these skills. Alternative procedures for doing laboratory investigations are all right in a curricular sequence. The alternatives can broaden students' skills. Alternative perspectives on interpretations and perhaps even some minor contradictions also may be acceptable from year to year. But silence is deadly. Without follow-up in each succeeding year, students' developing skills will atrophy. Science teachers in a high school or a school district ought to reach agreement on which outcome components and content understandings are really crucial for their students. Since it is unlikely that everything can be done well, teachers might concentrate on agreed priorities across the sequence of science courses.

3. The curriculum should provide students opportunity to develop quantitative and symbolic understanding in at least one field of science.

The natural sciences generally display their most impressive powers at the quantitative and symbolic levels: the power of well-structured knowledge that furnishes deep and fundamental understanding of a large range of natural phenomena; the power of dependable knowledge that leads to predictions that are confirmed with a high degree of reliability; the power of explanations that yield a satisfying view of the natural world. Students can appreciate these powers fully only through study that enables them to develop their quantitative and symbolic understanding. Moreover, collegiate study presupposes the development of some understanding at these levels. High schools usually offer this opportunity in a chemistry or physics course, but those are not the only alternatives. Developing quantitative and symbolic understanding through study in the life sciences would be equally appropriate.

4. The curriculum should provide students opportunity to acquire detailed knowledge in at least one field of science.

Just as the development of students' understanding in a science field at quantitative and symbolic levels enables them to appreciate fully the powers of the natural sciences, so too does the detailed, in-depth study of a science. Detailed knowledge involves the basic factual information of the field, its central concepts, its empirical laws and principles, and its major theories. All levels of understanding, from descriptive through symbolic, are represented. Students would ordinarily acquire detailed knowledge in the same science field in which they develop quantitative and symbolic understanding. However, other course sequences are possible.

The crucial matter in designing courses to provide such detailed knowledge is to select a limited number of topics that can provide the opportunity to develop students' science understanding and skills, and to focus sufficient attention on those topics so that this opportunity will be realized. The following lists from *Academic Preparation for College* may be useful in selecting a few such topics:

- In *biology* such detailed knowledge includes the central concepts, principles, and basic factual material of most, if not all, of the following topics: molecular and cellular aspects of living things, structure and function in plants and animals, genetics, evolution, plant and animal diversity and principles of classification, ecological relationships, and animal behavior.

- In *chemistry* such detailed knowledge includes the central concepts, principles, and basic factual material of most, if not all, of the following topics: states of matter, structure of matter, solutions, reactions of matter (including acid-base and oxidation-reduction), stoichiometry, energy changes in chemical reactions, equilibrium, kinetics, and descriptive chemistry (including periodic classification, metals, nonmetals, and introductory organic chemistry).

- In *physics* such detailed knowledge includes the central concepts, principles, and basic factual material of most, if not all, of the following topics: mechanics, optics, wave phenomena, electricity and magnetism, heat and kinetic theory, atomic and nuclear physics, and relativity.

Applying the Criteria

These criteria for formulating and selecting a high school science curriculum can be applied in many ways. This is why we believe they can be useful to teachers and other local decision makers responsible for translating large intentions into actual practice in the context of the possibilities, problems, and resources available to particular high schools. In developing the science statement in *Academic Preparation for College* and in elaborating it in this book, we have tried to keep in mind that many high schools face limited resources. We are determined that this scarcity of resources should be a temporary phenomenon, but until it is alleviated, we cannot ignore the fact that many students are currently enrolled in high schools with severely restricted possibilities. Somehow these students must receive adequate preparation in science so that they may have a fair chance for success in college. To be practical, in some situations a curricular plan may have to be extremely modest.

We suggest that the minimum possible application of the foregoing criteria would be that every college-bound student receives at least one full-year course that combines intensive, detailed work with selected topics in a particular field of science with quantitative and symbolic work in that field. Even this minimal possibility is, however, subject to some serious caveats. First, we are concerned here about all students who should be afforded the opportunity for college, a group considerably larger than the students currently enrolled in the "academic track." Moreover, the fact is that not even most students currently enrolled in the academic track are receiving this minimal level of preparation in science. Further, all that we have said about the importance of sufficient time to master the outcome components described in Chapter 2 suggests that it will be difficult for many, if not most, students to attain the needed learning outcomes by means of a single, one-year course in any field of science.

Second, it is quite unlikely that students will be successful in even the minimal precollegiate science course without extensive prior work in science at the descriptive and qualitative levels. The first criterion in this chapter was that students must be afforded the opportunity to develop all four varieties of scientific understanding, and in Chapter 2 we emphasized that descriptive and qualitative understanding were both important in themselves and necessary foundations for quantitative and symbolic understanding. Indeed, the typical introductory biology course rarely reaches the quantitative and symbolic levels. It will be necessary to design a new or an additional biology course if students are to develop all four varieties of understanding in the context of the study of biology.

Finally, we reiterate the point made in *Academic Preparation for College* that even if all students entering college received this minimal preparation in science, it would be inadequate for some of them. Students who aspire to major in scientific fields in college will need additional quantitatively based science in high school. Since the Educational EQuality Project is committed to increasing the number of low-income and minority students who prepare for careers in science, we do not see this caveat as a negligible matter. We conclude that the minimal curricular strategy of providing all potential college students with at least one science course incorporating both detailed knowledge and quantitative and symbolic understanding may be practical because it is modest with respect to the resources it requires. But this approach is anything but modest in terms of the skill and ingenuity it demands of high schools, nor can we afford to let it become modest in its aspirations for all students.

The science teachers at Paul Sabatier High School adopted a much more expansive approach to the science curriculum. The basic plan is a required core science program. The following description appears in the school's student handbook.

> The core program in science begins in the ninth grade and consists of a sequential study of the disciplines in physical science and in life science. Students study in both areas in parallel, and several alternative learning experiences are always provided. . . . In the main, the several disciplines are introduced in the approximate order of their historical appearance in modern science. This order helps each student to develop some notion of the evolution of scientific thought. Once a discipline is introduced into the sequence and its historical development is reviewed, the treatment of the subject matter is in the terms of the present-day structure of the discipline. In physical science, the sequence of disciplines studied begins with astronomy; in life science, the sequence begins with human biology. The subject matter of each of these disciplines early engaged man's attention for investigation by processes of observation and qualitative reasoning. In the initial study of astronomy and human biology, however, only the descriptive data and main questions for inquiry in the discipline are developed, since both these disciplines incorporate many ideas and principles from the other disciplines in physical science and in life science, respectively. For this reason, the sequence of studies in physical science returns in the end to astronomy, and the sequence in life science culminates with

a return to human biology. These disciplines now receive thorough treatments that highlight quantitative relationships and the main conceptual structures. This completes the sequence of studies in physical science and in life science up to the twelfth-grade proficiency level.

This plan for a high school science curriculum differs markedly from the customary offering of largely independent, year-long courses, most commonly arranged in a biology-chemistry-physics sequence. It differs even more strikingly from the minimal possibility we have just discussed, although it shares one important characteristic. It is intended for all students in the high school; it does not consign some students to receiving inadequate academic preparation for college.

Obviously, such a fundamental reorganization should not be undertaken without a thorough examination of the existing curriculum and careful consideration of the proposed change. The teachers of Paul Sabatier High did have a good rationale for their curricular plan. The sequence of courses deliberately mirrors the evolution of the sciences, starting with the chiefly descriptive and qualitative phases of science and moving on to increasingly intricate discipline structures and more comprehensive conceptual schemes. In doing so, the curriculum provides students with ample opportunity for descriptive and qualitative work in the sciences, work that will also provide a solid foundation for quantitative and symbolic understanding. The plan not only makes possible introducing the outcome components described in Chapter 2, but also permits recurring to them at increasing levels of sophistication. The curricular plan designed by the Paul Sabatier science teachers illustrates that numerous possibilities for the organization and content of the science curriculum are available and that no single way is necessarily the best under all circumstances. Whether this approach enables students in the particular circumstances of Paul Sabatier High to achieve the needed learning outcomes will ultimately, of course, have to be determined by its results.

Some observers will note that the curricular approach adopted at Paul Sabatier High School involves a strong distinction between the physical and life sciences, a distinction that could be inconsistent with recent developments in science. Biochemistry, for example, has developed as a rich and flourishing field in its own right. One curricular approach that may make possible closer attention to the connections and changing relations among the traditional fields of science was outlined in the *Report from a Conference on Goals for Science and Technology Education Grades K–12*, prepared for the National Science Board Commission on Precollege Education in Mathematics, Science, and Technology. With respect to courses intended to provide direct academic preparation for college, the conference suggested that "more balance in the development of facility in the disciplines could be achieved if each discipline was taught for part of each year, for instance on the basis of three periods of biology and two each of chemistry and physics in grade 11 and three periods of physics or chemistry and two each of the other subjects in grade 12 according to the students' interest."[2]

While this approach could offer the possibility of fresh attention to the evolving relations among the science disciplines, it also presents the possibility that students' study of science could end up a year-long miscellany of unconnected units. As the four criteria suggested in this chapter make evident, we believe that the first concern of a science curriculum should be to provide ample opportunity for the integrated development of science skills and understanding, not the abstract coordination of various units of science "content." We would urge those who consider the approach outlined above to give special attention to the question of whether this proposed curriculum contributes to all the outcomes described in Chapter 2. That would involve considering how well the various parts of the curriculum can be linked—in students' minds—by the unifying concepts of the sciences.

Further Considerations: Mathematics

Adequate academic preparation in science is linked closely to preparation in mathematics. Students preparing to major in one of the sciences in college will need to have completed advanced courses in the high school mathematics curriculum. These two considerations argue for close coordination between high school teachers of

---

2. National Science Board Commission on Precollege Education in Mathematics, Science, and Technology, *Educating Americans for the 21st Century: Source Materials* (Washington, D.C.: National Science Foundation, 1983), p. 31.

science and of mathematics as they plan their respective curricula. Moreover, Chapter 4 of *Academic Preparation in Mathematics* suggests that mathematics instruction give more attention to applications involving the solution of real-world problems. While the examples given there are not particularly relevant to the science curriculum, closer curricular coordination between high school mathematics and science teachers can locate areas in which such applications might reinforce students' work in both subjects. In this connection it may be particularly worthwhile to pay attention to the preclassroom, commonsense beliefs that students actually hold concerning the natural world.

Further Considerations: Social Studies

Academic Preparation in Social Studies suggests that high school study in that area needs to return from a preoccupation with topics of current interest to a closer fidelity to history and the social science disciplines as they are understood and taught in college. The very impact that science and technology are having on our society makes a similar caution appropriate with respect to high school study of the natural sciences. The Green Book emphasizes that understanding and evaluation of the complex social issues raised by scientific and technological developments require "a knowledge and understanding of science and its methods." We believe that just as history and the social sciences have something important to say in the discussion of these issues, so must the authentic voice of science be heard in such discussions. For example, students will not develop the needed "ability to distinguish between scientific evidence and personal opinion" without a science curriculum that provides for the learning outcomes described in Chapter 2 of this book. Such learning is what science teachers have been trained to provide, and it is part of what students need to acquire.

Preparing a greater number and diversity of students for success in college is itself an important social issue. It would be seriously misleading to foster the impression that mere discussion of science-related social issues constitutes such preparation in science. However it is shaped, the high school science curriculum must provide

45

students with a fair beginning to understanding science and its methods.

Moreover, the science processes described in Chapter 2 contribute directly to what the Green Book calls the Basic Academic Competencies, particularly the competencies in observing, mathematics, and reasoning. Chapter 5 of this book will discuss this relationship in some detail. Here we simply note that the Basic Academic Competencies are necessary preparation not only for college but for employment and other aspects of life beyond education. We suggest that precisely by helping students learn to engage in the processes of scientific investigation, the high school science curriculum will prepare them to participate in society in many different ways.

In short, the important social issues raised by science and technology do not seem good reason to confuse the high school science curriculum with a current topics version of the social studies curriculum. Social issues involving science and technology can waken some students' interest in natural science, and with great skill on the part of teachers, that interest can be channeled toward genuine science learning. These considerations, however, should find their place within a high school science curriculum that begins where the science statement in *Academic Preparation for College* begins: "Science—the study of the natural world—is both useful and rewarding in its own right."

IV. Teaching Science

This chapter illustrates how some science teachers have been working successfully to help students achieve the learning outcomes discussed in Chapter 2. We have chosen illustrations that both represent the most commonly taught science courses and fit comfortably into a variety of curricular settings. They show teachers working with ordinary, middle-range high school students—students whose academic preparation in science often needs improvement. A common theme in these instructional sequences is that the teachers proceed deliberately. Although science learning often involves considerable spontaneity, the exercises here are targeted to specific outcome components—those for which the teachers have discovered that their students need special attention. The teachers try to make the point of a particular exercise and its relation to the learning outcomes described in Chapter 2 explicit and clear to the students. Students seem to learn best when they know how what they are currently doing fits in with their study in the whole course. These illustrations are not meant to be prescriptive, but simply suggestive. Indeed, we hope that you will carefully consider and try out these approaches with your students. When you have found approaches that are effective with the students you teach, you can make them a part of your regular practice.

Investigating Motion

Earlier we suggested that it is important for students to have ample experiences with the several varieties of science understanding. Here is an instructional sequence that guides students through the four levels of understanding while dealing with a single topic: motion. Students begin with description and continue with activities involving qualitative and quantitative understanding. At the end of the sequence, they get an introduction to symbolic understanding. Many people hold the persistent misconception that a constant unbalanced force is always needed to keep an object moving with constant velocity. Such commonsense beliefs interfere with students' success in acquiring and applying scientifically correct principles of motion. The descriptive part of this sequence, and particularly its hypothesis formulation step, can prepare students to grapple with such everyday beliefs concerning motion. The effects of friction may even produce a situation that appears to confirm their commonsense notion. Later in the sequence, they will have a strikingly contradictory experience of acceleration, an experience then consolidated by reference to Newton's second law. This part of the sequence requires that teachers be particularly alert. It does not ask students to follow the usual approach of inducing Newton's second law from their experience. Rather, teachers introduce this principle of motion, and students work deductively with it. They bring it to bear as a frame of reference that accounts for their surprising experience of acceleration and integrates that experience into a larger and stable body of knowledge. Overall, this investigation of motion thus can contribute to several student competencies discussed in Chapter 2 under Outcomes A, B, C, and D, and, in general, to understanding the unifying concepts of the sciences (F.1).

Directions to students: You should work in a small group for this series of investigations. Let's start by asking, what happens to an object when a constant force is exerted on it?

Begin the investigation by setting up the apparatus, which consists of a board, a wooden block, a pulley, a string, a bucket, and some sand (see Figure 4.1). The pulley is attached to one end of the board and the block is placed on the opposite end. The string is attached to the empty bucket, which hangs free.

When the apparatus is ready to go, each student in your group should make a prediction about how the block will move when some sand is put into the bucket. Record your predictions on an appropriate data sheet. Write down what you think will really happen. Do your predictions indicate a single speed or that the speed will increase (acceleration)? When everyone has finished writing, one of you should slowly add some sand to the bucket until it begins to move. Let the block slide across the board until it reaches the end; then stop it with your hand. Now record your observations about the motion of the block. When everyone has finished recording, discuss the observations with each other. Is there fairly good agreement about what was observed?

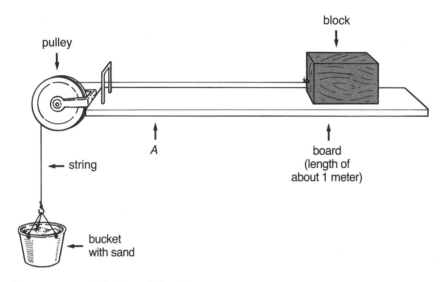

Figure 4.1   Block-and-bucket apparatus

It is usually a good idea to repeat an experiment several times to be sure that your observations are accurate and complete. Another person should empty the bucket and then slowly add some sand to it until the bucket begins to move. Record your observations. Then let a third person repeat the experiment. With the other members of your group, compare your original predictions about the motion of the block with your later observations. How are they the same? How are they different? Based on what you have observed, describe what happens to an object when an externally applied force is exerted on it.

The next step is to investigate what happens to an object when the constant force applied by the string is removed. You should use the same apparatus and basic procedures, but when the block reaches point A, one member of the group should catch the bucket of sand with his or her hand. When this is done, force is no longer exerted on the block by the string. Again, you should first make and record your predictions and then, afterward, your observations about the motion of the block. Discuss what you observe and repeat the procedure several times. After your discussion, describe what happens to an object when a net constant force no longer acts on it.

Now that you have had some practice observing and describing the motion of an object as that might involve speed and acceleration, you should use a different apparatus to gather information that will let you compare how objects move when one of the conditions is changed. Figure 4.2a shows the apparatus for this activity. You will need a force gauge made from a 5-by-7-inch index card, a rubber band, a paper clip, a small toy cart, and some masking tape to form a track on the floor. One member of your group should place the cart at the beginning of the track and pull on it with a small constant force as it goes along the length of the track. Record your observations about the motion of the cart as it moves along the track. You may be surprised by what happens, but write down exactly what you observe.[1] Repeat this procedure two more times, first using a medium constant force and then a large constant force to pull the cart along the track. Repeat the experiment as often as necessary to get a complete set of observations. Now discuss with your group how the motion of the cart is the same when you apply different amounts of force to it and how the motion is different.

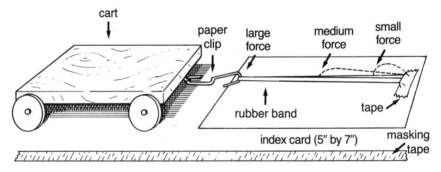

Figure 4.2a   Cart pulled by simple force gauge (qualitative)

---

1. Note to the teacher: Students who expected the cart to move at a constant speed are likely to be surprised by its startling acceleration. This unpredicted observation can open the door to revising their understanding of motion.

Try to summarize your observations in the form of a statement telling how an object moves (its speed or acceleration) when a small, medium, or large constant force is exerted on it.

Now you will have an opportunity to make some measurements and record some quantitative data. Once again, you should use the cart-and-track apparatus. This time, as shown in Figure 4.2b, use a spring scale calibrated in newtons in place of your index-card force gauge. Using a balance, find the mass of the cart in kilograms. Now find the mass in kilograms of three loads—one small, one medium, and one large—that will fit into the cart. It is convenient to use rolls of nickels as the load. Each roll of nickels has a mass of 0.20 kilograms. Add the mass of the cart and each load; record these combined masses as shown in Table 4.1. One person in your group should now pull the cart with the small load along the track with a small constant force. Again, you may be surprised by what happens. Continue the investigation by varying the force and the load until, for each size load, you have recorded data for each size force.[2]

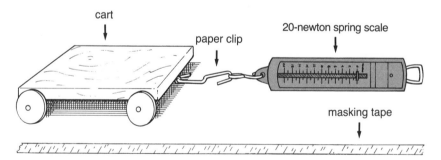

Figure 4.2b   Cart pulled by force-measuring spring scale (quantitative)

---

2. Note to the teacher: Here again, students whose expectations and predictions focused on velocity will be surprised by their observations of acceleration. Moreover, they will begin to notice that, for the various forces and loads about which they are recording data, acceleration seems to be different.

Table 4.1   Data for cart pulled by spring scale

Force (newtons)	Mass (cart + load) (kg)	Acceleration (m/sec/sec)*
Small		
5.00 N	2.00 kg	2.50 m/s/s
5.00 N	2.00 kg	1.67 m/s/s
5.00 N	2.00 kg	1.25 m/s/s
Medium		
7.50 N	2.00 kg	3.75 m/s/s
7.50 N	3.00 kg	2.50 m/s/s
7.50 N	4.00 kg	1.88 m/s/s
Large		
10.0 N	2.00 kg	5.00 m/s/s
10.0 N	3.00 kg	3.33 m/s/s
10.0 N	4.00 kg	2.50 m/s/s

* Expressing the units in this form will help beginning students grasp the concept of acceleration. More advanced students, of course, learn to use m/s².

Completing the table by calculating the acceleration of the cart in each trial may help you understand what has happened. Use the equation for Newton's second law, $F = ma$.[3] Since you measured the force applied and the mass of the object in each trial, you should be able to calculate the acceleration.

Explore Newton's second law further by using the data from your table to complete two graphs. The first graph, showing the rela-

---

3. Note to the teacher: By introducing Newton's second law at this point you provide students with a means of taking into account their surprising observations of acceleration. Students were not asked to measure and record data about acceleration—only about force and mass. They are not being asked at this point to induce the second law from their observations. They are provided with the second law and asked to make calculations about acceleration. This establishes a context into which their earlier surprising experiences with acceleration can be incorporated. In this way the second law itself becomes more plausible and likely to be understood, employed, and retained.

tionship between force and acceleration for the three different loads, is set up as shown in Figure 4.3a with force (in newtons) on the *x* axis and acceleration (in meters per second squared) on the *y* axis. There will be a line on your graph for the 2-kg load, a line for the 3-kg load, and a line for the 4-kg load. The second graph,

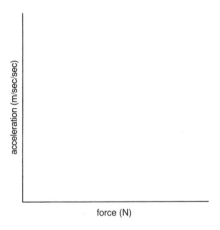

Figure 4.3a   Relationship between force and acceleration

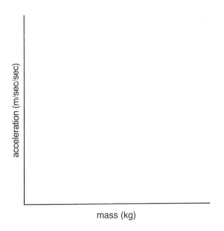

Figure 4.3b   Relationship between mass and acceleration

representing the relationship between mass and acceleration for the three sizes of force, is set up as shown in Figure 4.3b with mass (in kilograms) on the x axis and acceleration (in meters per second squared) on the y axis. There will be a line on your graph for the small force, one for the medium force, and one for the large force. Now, using your data in Table 4.1 and both sets of graphs, answer the following questions.

1. How is the acceleration of the cart related to the force you exert on it? What is the quantitative relationship between the cart's acceleration and the force?
2. How is the acceleration of the cart related to the mass of the cart? What is the quantitative relationship between the cart's acceleration and its mass?
3. How do the force and the mass together relate to the acceleration of the cart?
4. How do the values you derived from the application of Newton's second law seem to relate to what you observed when working with the cart-and-track apparatus? How do they relate to what you originally expected to happen?

In your work thus far, you've learned quite a bit about the concepts of force, mass, and acceleration and about the relationships among these concepts. Scientists have developed ways to represent a lot of knowledge with just a few symbols. It is useful at this point in your investigation of motion to summarize your knowledge in the way scientists do. Examine the symbols in the statement

$$\vec{F} = m\vec{a}$$

This statement contains just six symbols—three letters, two arrows, and an equal sign—yet it communicates a great deal of meaning. The letter symbols are not just letters of the alphabet. The letter F refers to the concept of force, m refers to the concept of mass, and a refers to the concept of acceleration. What scientists know about each of these concepts goes along with the letter symbol. That includes the exact definition of the concept, the methods of measuring it, how it is connected with other concepts, and so forth. The arrows over the F and the a communicate that force and acceleration are vector quantities—each has both magnitude and direction. The symbol m has no arrow, and this communicates that mass is a scalar quantity—it has only magnitude.

The equal sign tells us the relationships among the three concepts of force, mass, and acceleration. The statement $\vec{F} = m\vec{a}$ tells you that the product of the mass of an object times the magnitude of its acceleration is equal to the magnitude of the force exerted on it, and that the force and the acceleration are in the same direction. (The expression $F = ma$ without the arrow signs relates the magnitudes of the quantities only.) The equal sign makes the statement $F = ma$ an equation, so you can use all the rules of mathematics to describe the relationships among the variables. For example, when the acceleration remains the same and the amount of mass increases, the amount of force must increase. In more precise mathematical terms, to produce constant a, F must change in direct proportion to m.

Now that you have learned something about how objects move when a constant force acts on them, statements made up of symbols like $\vec{F} = m\vec{a}$ can be very useful and meaningful. As you learn more about motion, these symbols will take on added meaning and you will probably need to use more symbols to express new ideas.

In this instructional sequence, the students explore motion through experiences designed to guide their thinking from descriptive to symbolic understanding. In the first investigation, involving the block and the bucket of sand, the questions and answers were at the descriptive level. The students observed objects and phenomena (Outcome A.1), described observations using appropriate language (A.2), organized their observations (C.1), and interpreted their observations (C.4) on the descriptive level of understanding. In the second investigation, the students used the cart-and-force-gauge apparatus to make qualitative comparisons of the cart's motion when small, medium, and large forces acted on it. Qualitative understanding came into play in the observations students recorded (A.2) and organized (C.1) as they did the investigation and in the interpretations of observations (C.4) they gave in response to the concluding questions. Quantitative understanding was engaged in the next in-

vestigation as students measured force with a spring scale and mass with a balance (A.4 and A.6), processed experimental data (A.5), organized the data (C.1), and presented the data in graphs (C.2).

At several points in this series of investigations of motion, the students made predictions and checked them—that is, they formulated working hypotheses (B.2) and evaluated hypotheses in the light of observations (D.1). In the closing discussion, several characteristics of symbolic understanding were taken up explicitly. Deductions from Newton's second law, one of the unifying concepts of the sciences (F.1), helped students consolidate understanding of their observations in the investigations. Overall, by investigating the same topic at successive levels of understanding, the students had the opportunity not only to modify and deepen their understanding of motion but also to experience the differences and possibilities of the several varieties of scientific understanding.

Chemical Composition

One advantage of detailing the components of the science learning outcomes outlined in the Green Book is that teachers can plan instructional sequences targeted to strengthen specific components of those outcomes. We have just identified the components emphasized in the Investigating Motion sequence—notably, hypothesis formulation and evaluation. Other instructional sequences can emphasize the development of different components. For instance, we could design laboratory experiences that primarily encourage students to use data to evaluate hypotheses and formulate appropriate generalizations.

In the following sequence, students go first to the laboratory to collect data about the composition of chemical compounds (Outcomes A.3 through A.7). After the data have been collected and properly organized (C.1), the students are asked questions to elicit generalizations based on the relevant supporting data (C.4, D.2, and D.3). In this case students use the data to arrive at the law of definite composition and the law of multiple proportions.

The nineteenth-century English scientist John Dalton proposed that chemical elements are composed of discrete fundamental particles, different for each element, and that compounds are formed *as unique combinations of these particles. He called these submicroscopic particles atoms. The laws of chemical composition, then, provide a cornerstone for the atomic theory of matter, one of the unifying concepts of the sciences (F.1). At the end of this instructional sequence, students are encouraged to explain how what they discover about chemical composition can be explained by the atomic theory (E.1 and E.3).*

Directions to students: In this exercise, you will see how data collected in the lab can be used to form generalizations. Our example deals with the composition (by mass) of chemical compounds.

First, determine the mass of magnesium and oxygen in a sample of magnesium oxide. To do this, take a strip of magnesium ribbon about 25 cm long and scrape off the surface of the ribbon so that it is free from oxide. Then find its mass to the nearest 0.05 g. Record this mass in an appropriate data table.

Next, fold the ribbon into a small bundle and place it in a covered crucible. Heat the crucible over a low flame, gradually raising the flame until the magnesium burns. Remove the flame from the crucible and open the lid with tongs for a few seconds to admit air. Repeat this heating and burning until the magnesium no longer glows.

Continue the heating for another minute or so and then allow the crucible to cool a little. Add 15 drops of water with a medicine dropper and notice the odor of the escaping gas. Reheat the crucible until all the liquid is gone. Then allow the crucible to cool to room temperature and find its mass. Repeat the reheating and cooling until you obtain a constant mass. Find the mass of the magnesium oxide that has been formed, to the nearest 0.05 g.

Now that you have the mass of the magnesium and the magnesium oxide, you can figure out the percentage of the mass of the compound that is magnesium. Record this percentage of magnesium in your notebook. Since magnesium and oxygen are the only two elements in magnesium oxide, you can figure out the percentage of the mass of the compound that is oxygen by subtracting the percentage of magnesium from 100 percent.

When you get together as a class, consider the effect of adding water to the originally formed substance. Then find out the percentages of magnesium and oxygen found by other laboratory groups who have done the same experiment. How good is the agreement among the groups? You will probably find some fluctuation in the results. How do you account for the fluctuation? On the whole, does it seem that the percentages of magnesium and oxygen are fairly constant?

As you know, it is difficult to get good agreement on data collected in a high school chemistry laboratory. The data in Table 4.2 are the results of many time-consuming experiments under carefully controlled conditions. These data represent four different compounds (labeled with numbers), each made up of two elements (labeled with capital letters). The recorded results show the mass of one element that combined with the mass of the other element in each trial.

Table 4.2 Composition by mass in several trials for four compounds

Compound 1: Elements A and B			Compound 2: Elements C and D		
Trial	Mass A	Mass B	Trial	Mass C	Mass D
1	2.0 g	16.0 g	1	12.0 g	32.0 g
2	0.5 g	4.0 g	2	3.0 g	8.0 g
3	1.7 g	13.6 g	3	3.6 g	9.6 g

Compound 3: Elements E and F			Compound 4: Elements G and H		
Trial	Mass E	Mass F	Trial	Mass G	Mass H
1	2.3 g	3.5 g	1	4.0 g	3.2 g
2	4.1 g	6.1 g	2	5.0 g	4.0 g
3	6.5 g	9.9 g	3	9.0 g	7.2 g

Question 1: Using Table 4.2, make a general statement about the proportion of each element making up the mass of each compound. Are the percentages of the elements always the same for a given compound?

At a later time, some further careful experiments used elements A and B. It was found that two different compounds, compounds

1 and 5, could be formed from elements A and B. Table 4.3 gives data on the composition (by mass) of compounds 1 and 5 and also gives data on several other compounds composed of two elements.

Table 4.3 Composition by mass of various compounds

Compound 1	Mass A 2.0 g	Mass B 16.0 g
Compound 5	Mass A 2.0 g	Mass B 32.0 g
Compound 6	Mass J 6.0 g	Mass K 8.0 g
Compound 7	Mass J 6.0 g	Mass K 16.0 g
Compound 8	Mass L 6.3 g	Mass M 3.5 g
Compound 9	Mass L 6.3 g	Mass M 7.0 g
Compound 10	Mass N 2.8 g	Mass O 1.6 g
Compound 11	Mass N 2.8 g	Mass O 3.2 g
Compound 12	Mass N 2.8 g	Mass O 4.8 g

Question 2: Using Table 4.3, make a statement about the ratio of the mass of element B in compound 1 to its mass in compound 5. Now make a general statement including the other sets of compounds. Does your statement describe all the compounds listed?

Question 3: Using what you know about the atomic theory, explain the general statements you made in response to questions 1 and 2. Are these statements consistent with the atomic theory? Explain.

Schleiden and Schwann's Cell Theory

While the last question of the Chemical Composition investigation asks students to relate their generalizations to the atomic theory, the outcomes emphasized in this instructional sequence and in the previous one on motion are not the building of theories. In Chapter 2, however, we indicated the importance of Outcome E, recognizing the role of observation and experimentation in the development of scientific theories. We also identified components of this outcome, including recognizing the need for theories (E.1), formulating a theory to accommodate known phenomena and principles (E.2), and specifying the phenomena and principles that a theory explains (E.3). This outcome also involves deducing new hypotheses from a theory, interpreting and evaluating the results of the experiments designed to test a theory, and formulating a revised theory when new observations warrant it (E.4, E.5, and E.6). These are not easy tasks for students. However, the more involved students can be in following the development of a theory, the more established their recognition of the role of observation and experimentation in such developments is likely to be. Such active involvement may also help students learn to consider and adjust their own commonsense assumptions—"everyday theories"—about the natural world.

The following instructional sequence lets your students participate vicariously in the formulation of a classic theory. They may find several features particularly helpful. Near the beginning of the sequence the text explains the purpose of studying Schleiden and Schwann's cell theory. At the head of each main segment are questions that can provide a conceptual structure as students study the segment. The questions can also be stimuli for helpful class discussions as students grapple with the reasoning that led to the early cell theory, deduced hypotheses from it, and tested those hypotheses. The sequence supports the text's verbal and logical treatment with hands-on laboratory experiences. Unless students have seen crystallization, it's difficult for them to reason about the concept; observing actual cells helps them think about the idea of a cell.

Presented at the descriptive and qualitative levels of science understanding, this exercise can nevertheless involve students thoroughly in the processes of theory building (E.1 through E.6) and hypothesis formulation and testing (B.2 and B.3). It can also help develop understanding of the cell theory (F.1) and the nature of scientific inquiry (F.2).

Directions to students: What was the origin of the important idea that living things are made up of cells? Did some scientist wake up one morning, jump out of bed, and "discover" the cell theory? Not at all. In fact, the fascinating story of the scientists whose work led to the formulation of the cell theory in the nineteenth century can help us understand what investigations in science are all about.

As you read the following story, you will be asked some questions that should help guide your thinking and start a class discussion about some points illustrated by this story. Many of the questions challenge you to think for yourself, gather information from other resources, and express and defend your own opinions. Here are the first two questions. Think about them as you read the beginning of the story.

- How do new techniques advance theory in science?
- Why didn't the first person who described cells, Robert Hooke in 1665, generate the idea that cells are essential components of living things?

Today most people are familiar to some extent with cells; they can name the different parts of cells, observe cells with a microscope, and tell you that cells are the basic building blocks of all living things. This was not always the case. Because cells are very small, you cannot see them with your unaided eye. Until the development of the technique for looking at small objects through lenses to make them appear larger, no one guessed that cells existed. Using a microscope, Robert Hooke made careful and detailed observations that in 1665 first described cells in a slice of cork. It was not until the 1800s, however, that scientists were able to give a meaningful interpretation to Hooke's interesting observations.

In the 1830s Robert Brown announced his discovery of the plant cell nucleus. Brown, however, did not recognize the importance of his discovery and made no use of it. This was done a few years later by Matthias Jakob Schleiden, a German botanist. One reason that Schleiden was able to formulate new ideas about cells was that he was working with an improved compound microscope. The materials for observation are supplied by nature, though nature often needs a little prodding by scientists using scientific instruments. The interpretation of observations, of course, can come only from scientists themselves. Although his microscope let Schleiden see more details of cells than had previously been seen, the cell theory did not suddenly unfold before him. In fact, Schleiden developed concepts that combined correct basic ideas with completely wrong details.

Here are some questions to think about as you read the second part of the story.

■ What kinds of things influence how scientists interpret what they observe?

■ How did Schleiden's choice of material to study influence what he inferred from his experiments and observations?

Schleiden decided that an important research questions was, "What is the origin of this particular small organism, the cell?" He chose to study the formation of cells in two of the reproductive parts of plants. Schleiden then made and recorded his observations of cell growth in the particular plant cells. What he recorded was a process during which new cells crystallized out of a surrounding clear solution. This is a remarkable idea, and it seems likely that Schleiden hit on the notion by watching the formation of inorganic crystals from their surrounding solutions.

You can see for yourself the crystallization process that Schleiden thought explained the formation of cells. One good way to do this is to observe crystals grow when a hot, saturated solution of sodium chlorate cools. Add 12 g of sodium chlorate to 10 ml of water in a test tube. Heat the water until all the sodium chlorate is dissolved. Using a medicine dropper, place a few drops of the hot, clear solution on a microscope slide and observe under low power. Crystals will begin to form as the solution cools. Why? (If crystals do not begin to form, add a grain of the sodium chlorate solid to the drops on the slide to start crystallization.) What shape and color do the crystals of sodium chlorate have? Are you watching a living or a nonliving process? Explain.

Schleiden, as it turned out, happened to have chosen an atypical material to study. The reproductive cells of plants do not grow as do most other cells. This unfortunate choice of material combined with his prior knowledge about the crystallization process led Schleiden to the incorrect inference that all cell growth was analogous to crystallization.

Here are questions that apply to the third part of the story.

- What is a hypothesis in science?
- How did Schwann's choice of material to study influence what he inferred from his experiments and observations?
- How do you think that Schleiden's work on plant cells influenced Schwann's observations of animal cells?

Thus far we have discussed the idea that plants are composed of cells. What about animals? Theodor Schwann was a German zoologist who in 1839 first advanced the theory that animals, like plants, also are composed of cells. Schwann reasoned that all living things are either plant or animal. If plants are made of cells, as Schleiden claimed, then perhaps animals also are made of cells. Schwann made many observations of various animal cells to determine if his hypothesis was correct.

Schwann thought that he could establish the existence of animal cells if he could demonstrate (1) that the elementary parts of animal tissue have nuclei and cell walls (the parts of plant cells described by Brown, Schleiden, and others) and (2) that the elementary parts of animal tissue grow in the same manner as plant cells (as described by Schleiden). To gather evidence, Schwann had to look at many different animal cells. You can appreciate the difficulties he faced if you examine various cells with a microscope. Prepared, stained slides are best for this, but you can make your own wet mounts of several kinds of animal cells. Here is one suggestion for preparing animal cells for microscopic viewing.

Place a frog in a jar containing 3 cm of water and allow it to stand for about four hours. The water will become cloudy with thin flakes from the outer layers of the frog's skin. With a needle, lift out a small piece of this material and place it in a drop of water on a clean microscope slide. Try to straighten out the material into a thin sheet and then stain it with fountain pen ink or methylene blue. Add a coverslip and observe the material under low power, then under high power. Can you see a cell boundary, a nucleus, and cytoplasm? Make a labeled drawing of one of the cells. Other convenient sources of animal cells are the inner lining of your cheek or a drop of frog's blood. Observe some of these cells under the microscope and make drawings of what you see.

The material that Schwann chose to study extensively was the notochord in frog larvae. He reported observing a cell wall and a nucleus in the cells of these notochords. This particular kind of animal cell happens to be atypical because it has a cell wall; most animal cells have no wall, but have a membrane enclosing the contents of the cell. Schwann thought, however, that his observations of these cells, with their cell walls and nuclei, were sufficient evidence to support the first part of his argument. He then proceeded to the second part: demonstrating that animal cells grow as plant cells do.

Schwann's description of the growth of cells in animal tissue is very similar to what Schleiden reported seeing in plant cells. The fact that the two scientists met and discussed Schleiden's notions before Schwann made his observations may shed some light on why Schwann observed what he did. In any case, Schwann was satisfied that he now had enough evidence to conclude that animal tissue is in fact composed of cells like the cells of plants.

Consider these questions as you read the last part of the story.

- In which ways is the cell theory of the 1980s different from Schleiden and Schwann's cell theory? In which ways is it the same?
- Why do scientists make up theories? How are scientific theories and hypotheses connected?
- When do scientists change their theories?

In this story, you have seen how a few scientists came up with an idea they thought explained the basic structure of living things. Their idea was that plants and animals are made up of tiny units called cells, which have a nucleus and a cell wall and crystallize out of a solution. They knew that if their idea was a really good one, they could use it to predict laboratory observations of any kind of living thing. Schleiden and Schwann then formulated hypotheses and tested them in the laboratory to gather evidence that would either support their idea or force them to change it.

As microscopes and staining techniques became more sophisticated, other scientists were able to gather information that led to a revision of the cell theory. For example, in 1858 Rudolph Virchow demonstrated that most cells reproduce by division of each cell into daughter cells rather than by cellular crystallization. Other researchers established that the cell wall is not an integral component of all living things. In particular, animal cells don't generally have cell walls though Schwann believed that they do. Of course, the cell wall is usually the most conspicuous part of the plant cell, and this is what Robert Hooke had originally observed in cork.

Researchers in cellular biology and related fields are constantly coming up with new hypotheses to test in the laboratory. The cell theory, like any scientific theory, is continually being tested, revised, and refined. As it stands today, it is the best current explanation for what living things are made of and how they function.

Using Vee Maps and Concept Maps

Besides understanding the process and techniques of scientific investigation, students also need to be able to organize and clarify what they learn in the laboratory as well as from textbooks and other instructional materials. Traditional note-taking and outlining are study techniques for helping students organize what they have learned in laboratory investigations and in discussions of science principles, laws, and theories. Here, we illustrate two additional approaches that may help students organize their ideas: concept mapping and Vee mapping. As science teachers have begun to try out these strategies, they are reporting promising results.

With regard to the outcomes of science instruction identified in Chapter 2, Vee maps contribute to the development of students' competence in organizing data and observations (C.1) and interpreting them (C.4). They also can contribute to competence in recognizing a problem (B.1), designing procedures for experiments (B.4), and understanding the nature of scientific inquiry (F.2). The concept mapping strategy, however, is designed primarily to develop the students' understanding of concepts (F.1), whether developed in the laboratory or met elsewhere. To explain the strategies, which were designed by Joseph Novak and D. Bob Gowin, we give an illustration of each.[1]

---

1. D. Bob Gowin and Joseph D. Novak, *Learning How to Learn* (New York: Cambridge University Press, 1984).

Directions to students: Now that you've experienced how laboratory activities can help you learn, I want to introduce some techniques to help you organize and clarify what you learn. One useful technique is called Vee mapping. It is a way of keeping track of what you do in the laboratory, why you're doing it, and what you find out. A Vee map was named because of its V shape. First you need to know the basic structure of any Vee map. Figure 4.4 shows the kinds of things included.

The left side of the Vee is the conceptual, or thinking, side. It will include the concepts important to the lab activity you are doing. In the middle of the Vee is a focus question, which tells what you are trying to find out. The right side of the Vee is the methodological, or doing, side. It will include what you do to answer the focus question and some claims about what you think the answer to the focus question might be.

I will illustrate Vee mapping by showing you an example made by a student named Joe. He was investigating what happens to ice water as it is heated (see Figure 4.5). On the left (thinking) side of the Vee, Joe listed the concepts he thought were important in this investigation. The list can be added to, whenever necessary, during and after the experiment. In the middle of the Vee, Joe wrote his focus question, "What happens to the temperature of ice water when I add heat?" Below the Vee, to describe the event that he was studying in the lab, Joe showed a bowl of ice water being heated. On the right (doing) side of the Vee, Joe put all the data he

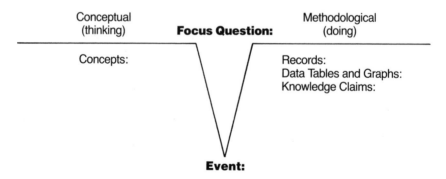

Figure 4.4   Vee map format

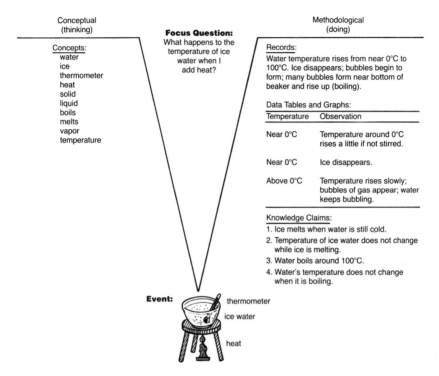

Figure 4.5   Vee map for heating ice water investigation

collected during the experiment—his observations and his measurements. Then he added the data table and graphs he made to help him interpret his data. Finally, he made some claims about how he thought the focus questions would be answered. Joe could have added principles and theories to the thinking side and included more detailed tables and observations on the doing side. As it was, however, the Vee map made clear what he was trying to find out, what he did, and what he actually found out.

Another way to organize and clarify what you learn in the laboratory is called concept mapping. Concept maps show relationships among concepts. After you finish your work in the laboratory, concept mapping is a way to summarize what you have learned.

Joe, the same student who did the ice water experiment, decided to make a concept map after he completed his Vee map. Figure 4.6 was Joe's first attempt at a concept map. First, Joe listed the concepts he used to think about what happens to ice water when it is heated. His list included solid, liquid, heat, temperature, water, and so on. After he had a fairly complete list, he began to link concepts that are related. To connect concepts, he drew lines and arrows between them and used such words as *is, when,* and *becomes* to describe how concepts are related. Joe used a piece of scrap paper and a pencil at first so he could erase lines and move concepts around until the map made the most sense to him.

If Joe decides to investigate what happens to ice water when it is heated at different atmospheric pressures, he will have to revise his concept map to show how pressure is related to the concepts already mapped. Like Joe, you should change or redraw concept maps whenever you discover new relationships between concepts and whenever your understanding of a relationship changes.

Now that you have seen an example of how Vee mapping and concept mapping can be used, you should try it out for yourself. You might try to map the important concepts involved in the chemical composition exercise we did before.

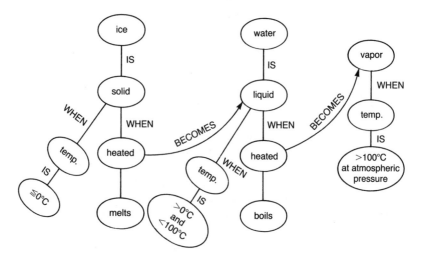

Figure 4.6   Concept map for heating ice water investigation

Concept mapping and Vee mapping may seem novel and unfamiliar techniques at first. The evidence does suggest that it takes time for students to acquire and begin to profit from them. Think of them, however, as potentially more economical and effective alternatives to the traditional study techniques of outlining and notetaking. You may want to try them. It can be helpful for many students to think explicitly about how what they learn is anchored in how it is learned and about the number and nature of the relationships among scientific concepts as well as among laws, principles, and theories.

V. Science and the Basic Academic Competencies

This chapter offers some suggestions about how the study of science can contribute to the development of the Basic Academic Competencies identified in *Academic Preparation for College*. Those Basic Academic Competencies are reading, writing, speaking and listening, observing, mathematics, reasoning, studying, and using computers.

Teachers in some fields worry that concern for the Basic Academic Competencies can distract needed attention from their particular subject. Therefore, it is important to illustrate how the development of the competencies is integral and necessary to work in specific subject areas. Chapter 2 of this book, in fact, has already indicated the close relationship between the science learning outcomes and the competencies of observing, mathematics, and reasoning. For instance, observing objects and phenomena (A.1) and describing observations using appropriate language (A.2) directly involve the observing component described in the Green Book as "the ability to see and to interpret things and events in nature . . . [and] in the laboratory . . . with reasonable accuracy, and to record such observations in appropriate form." The whole of Outcome B, which concerns formulating and testing hypotheses, could virtually be paraphrased in terms of the following part of the reasoning competency: "the ability to identify and formulate problems, as well as the ability to propose and evaluate ways to solve them." Formulating empirical laws or principles warranted by the relationships found (D.2) is an instance of the ability to use inductive reasoning, while deducing new hypotheses from a theory (E.4) explicitly refers to the ability to use deductive reasoning.

We note, moreover, that the techniques of Vee mapping and concept mapping introduced in Chapter 4 can contribute to a crucial study skill in science: clarifying and retaining understanding of the relationships among observations and broad concepts. The rest of this chapter, therefore, discusses how science learning can be related to the remaining Basic Academic Competencies: reading, writing, speaking and listening, as well as computer competency.

Expanding the Laboratory with Microcomputers

With the increasing availability of versatile and affordable microcomputers, many science teachers have the opportunity to consider how the use of this pervasive technological innovation can enhance science learning. Various possibilities have been suggested, but not all seem to offer immediate help. A barrage of computer programs, or software, in science has been produced for the microcomputer hardware that schools have purchased. As we write this, the science instructional software available for drill, tutorials, testing, or guiding students in solving problem exercises has seldom been shown to be more effective than other, more usual modes of instruction. Consequently, we are cautious about recommending the general use of computers for these purposes at the present time.

The case is different, however, when it comes to using microcomputers to expand students' laboratory experiences. Microcomputers already offer students opportunities for investigations never before possible in schools. Such opportunities are bound to increase as appropriate software and hardware continue to be developed. A simulation is one way to use microcomputers to expand school laboratory experiences. The following instructional sequence on plant competition illustrates this use. It is adapted from a unit developed by the Chelsea Science Simulation Project.[1] Note that in this sequence the computer simulation is only a part of the instruction. Part A prepares the students for the simulation with a graphing exercise that parallels the graphs they will see and use in the simulation. In parts B and C, guide questions calling for thought and written responses help students interpret the simulated experiments. This approach helps anchor use of the computer in the overall development of science learning. Computer competency,

1. M. E. Leveridge, *Chelsea Science Simulations Plant Competition COMPETE* (London: Edward Arnold, 1982). Distributed by CONDUIT, University of Iowa.

like all the Basic Academic Competencies, can and should be developed as an integral part of work in science, not as an extraneous and a potentially distracting addition.

A. Plant Growth

For many centuries human beings have recognized that plants interact with one another. The commonest form of interaction arises when plants compete for some resource whose supply is insufficient for their needs. Competition can occur within a single plant, or between plants of the same or different species.

Most plants grow in soil. They must obtain all their requirements for growth from this soil and from the air above it. The availability of each resource depends not only on how much is present in a plant's surroundings, but also on how many other plants are growing there. The more plants there are, the less of each resource there is available for each plant.

A quantitative study of plant growth depends on some way of measuring that growth. There are several possible methods, each with advantages and disadvantages. Ashby used four methods to study the growth of oats.[2] He soaks 100 oat grains for one day and then planted them. Groups of 10 plants were harvested and measured at weekly intervals after planting. His results are given in Table 5.1.

Plot a graph of each of these measurements of growth against the time since the oats were planted. The graphs can be compared most easily if they are drawn together on the same side of the graph paper, but you will need to use four different vertical axes.

−A.1   To what extent do these measurements show similar patterns of growth?

−A.2   What are the advantages and disadvantages of each of these as measurements of growth?

−A.3   The dry mass of the plants is the most commonly used measurement of growth. Is it likely to be a good method for the farmer to judge the degree of success of the crops? Give reasons for your answer.

2. Eric Ashby, "Some Obsolete School Botany," *School Science Review* 19 (March 1938): 409–418.

Table 5.1   Data from Ashby's experiment on the growth of oats

Time from planting (d)	Height (mm)	Number of leaves	Wet mass (g)	Dry mass (g)
0	—	—	0.07	0.041
7	—	—	0.11	0.029
14	95	1	0.21	0.033
21	170	2	0.36	0.044
28	253	3	0.87	0.095
35	380	4	1.94	0.177
42	485	8	4.05	0.380
49	550	10	8.35	0.760
56	657	13	17.00	1.500
63	758	26	30.30	2.430
70	850	48	60.80	5.100

B. Simulated Growth in Monoculture

In recent years many experimental investigations have analyzed the ways in which plants interact. Cultivated plants have often been used, since a full understanding of the factors affecting their growth is of considerable economic importance. Investigations of this type are not difficult to carry out, but they can require more time and space than are available in schools. The computer program COMPETE simulates plant growth to enable you to investigate some of the factors affecting plant competition in a much shorter time.

The simulation is based on outdoor experiments in the Netherlands with real plants of four kinds—barley, *Hordeum* sp. oats, and dwarf and tall varieties of field pea. Baeumer and De Wit grew the plants in rows in a heavy but well-structured clay soil. The tall peas were supported by wire gauze 120 cm high. There was sufficient rainfall during the experiments to ensure that the plants were not short of water. The plants were kept from weeds by herbicides and weeding.[3]

---

3. K. Baeumer and C. T. De Wit, "Competitive Interference of Plant Species in Monocultures and Mixed Stands," *Netherlands Journal of Agricultural Science* 16 (1968): 103–122.

In COMPETE you can choose the kind of plant you wish to grow and the density of planting. The distance between the rows is used to measure this density. The growth is measured as the dry mass of the aerial parts of the plants per square meter at intervals from day 36 to day 78 after planting. In the questions that follow, the dry mass on day 78 is called the final dry mass, although growth continues after this time.

When you first use COMPETE, it is best to type START when *Option ?* appears on the screen. You will then be guided through the program. Grow one kind of plant on its own, that is, in monoculture. To obtain the kind of plant, type BARLEY, OATS, DWARF, or TALL. Use a row spacing of 100 cm. Figure 5.1 shows an example of the results you will see on the screen.

When *Option ?* appears again on the screen, you can alter the values you chose by using a series of keywords. Type MONO to select a single plant for study. Type ROW to change the distance apart of the rows. Type PLANT to change the kind of plant you are working with. Select one kind of plant and use the computer

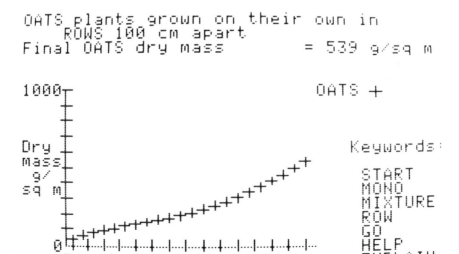

Figure 5.1   Graph display from COMPETE program

to simulate its growth at several different planting densities. Suitable values are row spacings of 25, 50, 100, 175, and 250 cm. The minimum row spacing is 20 cm, and the maximum is 500 cm.

–B.1 Compare the growth from day 36 to day 78 with that which must have taken place in the first 35 days. Was this early growth at a faster or a slower rate?

Make two graphs from the results of your investigations. In the first, plot the final dry mass per square meter against the row spacing. In the second, plot the final dry mass per meter length of the row against the row spacing.

–B.2 What effect does the closer spacing have on the final dry mass per square meter? What effect does the closer spacing have on the final dry mass per meter length of the row? Explain these effects.

If time permits, repeat the work with a different kind of plant and summarize the similarities and differences between the growth of the plants.

C. Plant Growth in Mixtures

The more densely plants grow, the greater is their interference with each other's growth. One of the main factors that is likely to be in short supply is light. A plant's ability to obtain light will depend partly on its height compared with that of its neighbors. Baeumer and De Wit grew mixtures of two kinds of plants at one time in alternate rows. The light reaching such a mixture is shown in Figure 5.2. The values given for the light intensity are percentages of the values above the plants.

–C.1 Which of these plants shown receive high and which receive low light intensities? Explain the reason for this.

The computer simulation can be used to study the interaction of any two of the four kinds of plants at different planting densities by typing the keyword MIXTURE. The different kinds are grown in alternate rows, so that there is 50 percent of each in the mixture. Select two kinds of plants and carry out an investigation aimed at answering the following questions. It is best to use the same planting densities as were used when plants were grown in monoculture.

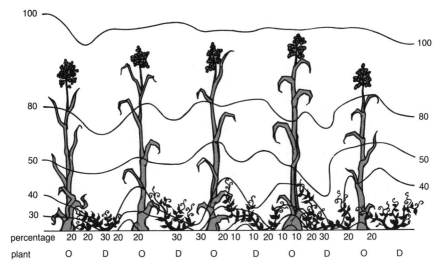

Figure 5.2 Percentage of light intensity at different heights in a mixture of two plants

With the mixtures, only half the number of plants of each kind are being grown, compared with the growth of the same kind of plant in monoculture at the same planting density. It is therefore necessary to double the final yields of each plant in a mixture to make it comparable with the final yields in monoculture.

−C.2 Which mixture did you investigate? Which of the kinds of plants gave the highest final yield? Is this what you would expect from the plants' heights?

−C.3 Compare the final yields per square meter of each kind of plant grown on its own with its final yield when grown in the mixture. Are the results what you expect from the plants' heights?

−C.4 Is the total final yield of your mixture ever greater than that of either kind of plant grown on its own?

If the growth of the two kinds of plants together results in a greater yield than either kind grown on its own, it seems at first sight that it would be an advantage for a farmer to grow crops in mixtures rather than on their own. This is sometimes done, but there are several disadvantages.

–C.5   What disadvantages to a farmer do you think there are in growing mixtures of two kinds of plants together in the same field, even if it gives greater yield?

*   *   *

In this instructional sequence, the simulation of plant competition allows students to change certain variables in the situation they are investigating and then to see quickly how the change affects the outcome of the experiment. This is typical of the various computer-simulated experiments now available for school use, though in many the outcome is displayed pictorially, sometimes with animation or as numerical data, as well as in graphs. The students' challenge is to interpret the data the simulated experiments generated and to arrive at warranted conclusions and generalizations (Outcome D.2). The simulations are also excellent vehicles for testing hypotheses (B.3 and D.1), since students can systematically manipulate variables and rerun or replicate experiments as often as they like. In the course of this investigation, students quite naturally exercise the computer competency outlined in *Academic Preparation for College*, particularly "some ability to use the computer and appropriate software for . . . simulations."

Using simulations places students in the position of genuine investigators, much as scientists are. These experiences can be effective in developing students' understanding, not only of the processes of scientific inquiry but also of the phenomena of the natural world. Indeed, you may want to reinforce a small part of the foregoing simulation exercise by actually growing the plants in the laboratory.

Another way to use microcomputers to expand school laboratory experiences is as efficient laboratory aids. Although it is most important that students learn to gather scientific data themselves, microcomputers can extend such activities to larger time frames and data ranges. With the proper software and auxiliary devices, which are not very complex and seldom expensive, school microcomputers can be put to work acquiring data, monitoring experiments, and processing data.

Using probes sensitive to changes in temperature, pressure, light intensity, or electrical conductivity, for example, the microcomputer can collect data from experimental setups, living organisms, or the environment. The computer can instantly display the data on its screen, plot a graph of the data points against time, or save the data on a magnetic disk for later analysis. Data can be collected continuously or intermittently over any desired period of time. With suitable programming, the computer can change variables in the experiment at specified times or under certain conditions. Once the data are collected, the computer performs the desired analyses and displays results, data tables, and graphs. The possibilities and variations for data processing are endless, limited only by the ingenuity of the software programmer. Computer use can mean that students will have more opportunity to experience scientific investigations than they ever had before. Developing computer competency can deepen, rather than distract from, their science learning.

The Verbal Competencies

Reading, writing, and speaking and listening are the currency of exchange in our science classrooms and laboratories, as in most classrooms. And yet, to a surprising extent, science teachers tend to take these student competencies for granted. We want to suggest that the perspectives developed in this book, as well as progress made in other disciplines, entitle these verbal competencies to fresh attention on the part of science teachers. Experts on language sometimes refer to reading and listening as the receptive competencies and to writing and speaking as the productive competencies. *Academic Preparation in English* makes the point that the development of these competencies is interrelated and that they develop best when the curriculum balances and integrates their practice. We want to suggest that science teachers also give more attention to balance between the productive and the receptive competencies and to their integration not only with each other but with science understanding. Too often students experience science courses as a jumble of rootless, unconnected vocabulary. Even worse, terminology can be connected to prior, commonsense notions that are quite different from what the teacher intended to convey. These misconceptions can actually interfere with students' science learning. In science, divorce of the verbal competencies from science understanding can be tantamount to no competency at all.

Reading

Students' laboratory and field experiences are of primary importance in science learning, but such learning also relies heavily on reading material, ranging from laboratory directions and science textbooks to journal articles and research reports. Because science students must be competent readers, it is important to ensure that their reading skills are appropriately developed. This means that reading skills must develop beyond mere recognition of words to involve genuine science understanding. Here it is relevant to cite an observation made in *Academic Preparation in Mathematics* with respect to the difficulty that many beginning high school students have in reading textbooks.

> Their problem is likely to be diagnosed as poorly developed reading skills. When help is provided, it often consists of remedial instruction in basic word recognition and literal comprehension. The underlying theory seems to be that if a certain set of basic reading skills is mastered, comprehension will take care of itself.
> This "deficit" theory of reading instruction . . . labels students as "problem readers" who may simply need experience in integrating and transferring their skills to the more sophisticated reading tasks. . . . In elementary school, students learn to read using textbooks in which the situations are familiar and the vocabulary easily understood, but a high school . . . textbook presents them with vocabulary in a context where skill in pronouncing an unfamiliar word will not help the student establish its meaning. Meaning depends upon experience, and students who lack experience with the concepts being discussed will not be able to understand the discussion, no matter how well their basic word-decoding skills are developed. . . . their real need is to develop both skills and understanding in the context of interesting new content.

This is why we believe that science learning should rest on a base of laboratory and field experience and that, insofar as possible, concepts should be developed by reference to that experience. Moreover, science concepts have connections to each other, and reading competence in science means understanding these relationships.

Two relevant components of reading competence in this connection are known technically as inferential comprehension and comprehension monitoring. *Inferential comprehension* involves integration, summarization, and elaboration. *Integration* means following textual inferences meaningfully. For example, one might read that Mary ate all the pizza and that she felt sick later. This leads to making the connection: "Oh, this means that Mary ate too much pizza and it made her feel bad." *Summarization* is the ability to glean the important ideas from a text passage and state them concisely. *Elaboration* is the process of bringing prior knowledge to bear on a text to expand its meaning. A competent reader uses *comprehension monitoring* to make sure that what is being read is understood. For example, the reader may slow the pace or reread a sentence or paragraph to understand it better. Both inferential comprehension and comprehension monitoring are necessary for a student to be a competent reader of science texts.

The concept mapping technique introduced in Chapter 4 is one way to help students develop these processes. To make a concept map of a given passage, the reader must identify the main ideas, or concepts, contained in the text and determine how they are related to each other. The completed concept map is, in effect, a summarization of the text. Because the process of making the map involves studying the relationships given in the text, the student must monitor comprehension in order to make the map.

We illustrate the use of a concept map to analyze text with a passage from a typical high school science textbook shown in Appendix B. The passage is part of an introductory chapter called "The Web of Life." It deals with a basic idea in biology, namely, that life is interconnected in an energy system. To begin the exercise, you could ask your students to read and analyze the introductory section. The first two highly descriptive paragraphs suggest that all living things are in some way related to one another, as in a web. This weblike integration of living things is the overall theme of the chapter. It might be diagramed as in Figure 5.3.

The third paragraph introduces the idea that energy flow is important in the balance and changes that occur in the web of life. The concepts of balance and change, which were discussed in a

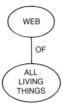

Figure 5.3   Concept map for biology text passages (see Appendix
            B): initial stage

previous passage, are not elaborated in Figure 5.3. The new concepts and relationships in paragraph three might yield additions to
your students' evolving concept map as shown in Figure 5.4.

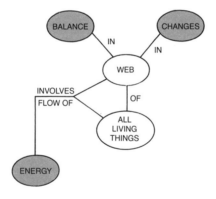

Figure 5.4   Concept map for biology text passage: intermediate
            stage

The fourth paragraph brings to light the idea that all living things
have some form of activity, while the fifth paragraph explains the
relationship between the activity of living things and energy. Anything that living things do requires energy. The fifth paragraph also
gives a scientific principle that energy can be neither created nor
destroyed. So far, the map might look like Figure 5.5 (see next
page).
The next part of the text involves the source of energy. The idea

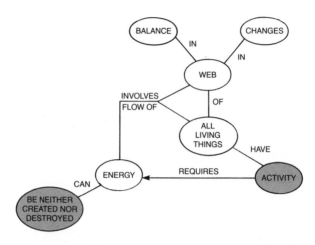

Figure 5.5   Concept map for biology text passage: further stage

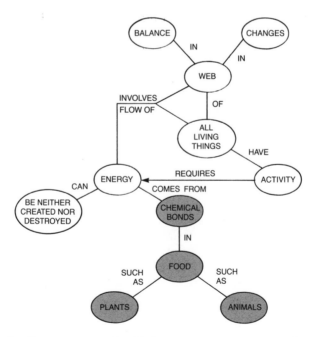

Figure 5.6   Concept map for biology text passage: nearly complete

that our energy comes from the food we eat is stated; the explanation is that food contains chemical bonds in which energy is stored. Humans eat both animal material (hamburgers) and plant material (potatoes) to satisfy their needs. Adding these ideas to the concept map might result in Figure 5.6.

The final two paragraphs of the passage state that animals get their energy by eating plants. Plants do not eat, but they get their energy from the light energy that comes from the sun. Integration of these concepts results in a completed concept map for this passage (Figure 5.7).

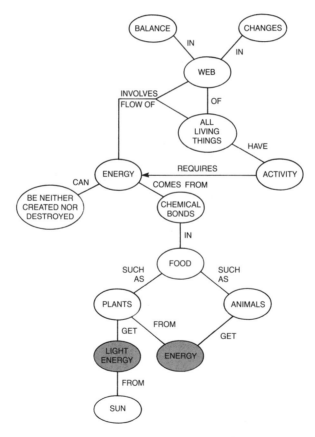

Figure 5.7   Completed concept map for biology text passage

At first glance, such a map may look like an illustration from a medieval treatise. But its greatest value lies not so much in the completed map as in the process of producing it. In creating the map, the student has had to exercise the processes of inferential comprehension and comprehension monitoring. In the words of *Academic Preparation for College*, the student has had to identify, comprehend, and summarize the main and subordinate ideas in a written work. More than that, the student has had to reproduce the relationship among science concepts actively and in a way that they can be readily recovered. Such maps, like texts themselves, can end up being only words on paper. When learning is grounded in some experience with the phenomena themselves, however, concept maps can be a valuable means toward reading with comprehension.

Writing

Attention to writing in the science classroom generally has been limited to preparing laboratory and field reports and answering examination questions. But a major change has been occurring with respect to the teaching of writing, and some science teachers have been not only altering how they approach writing but finding new roles for it in science learning. They approach writing as "thinking on paper" and report that it improves students' retention of what they have learned. This approach begins with the basic insight that writing is not a matter of applying some accumulation of "mechanics" to preexisting thought. Rather, writing is seen as a process of formulating, clarifying, and refining thought and expression simultaneously. *Academic Preparation in English* elaborates this view of writing as process in the following way.

> . . . student writing . . . must be understood as something that happens through a process or flow of activities, not as a static or prestanding structure that one attempts to reproduce on the page. This view of writing includes the following points.

> ■ Writing is a process that involves analyzing the writing task and the intended audience, focusing an idea, examining what one knows and needs to know about the topic, gathering necessary information, organizing and drafting thought, shaping and reshaping the draft, and

editing the final product with regard to purpose, subject, audience, and the relation to standard written English. We organize this flow of activity into the stages of prewriting, writing, and postwriting.

- Over extended periods of teaching time, this process incorporates other activities including observing, talking, listening, note taking, and practice in information gathering. . . .
- Mere frequency of writing alone helps little to increase student ability. Therefore, we attempt to make the writing process recursive—that is, throughout the curriculum we have students return several times to similar tasks. This method takes into account how ability deepens gradually over time and provides a realistic background for the appraisal of performance and assessment of development.

Science teachers may find this view of writing as a process quite promising. For instance, the prewriting stage takes in the large amount of ad hoc writing that science students already do. They record laboratory and field observations; they take notes on readings, lectures, and discussions. Seeing writing as a process would help fit these activities into a larger whole. An expert on writing might stress that in getting words on paper, the student has already begun the process of writing, a flow of activity that leads to fuller understanding and expression. The process approach to writing can substitute a streamlined flow for the notorious writer's block. From the viewpoint of the science teacher, the larger whole into which these student writing activities fit is, of course, the overall process of scientific thought. Chapter 2 of this book tried to clarify the role of observation and description in that regard.

Both the process of scientific thought and the process of writing involve further activities of organization and integration. There is reason to hope that these aspects of the two processes could be mutually refining. Sometimes student laboratory or field reports can be accurate with regard to particulars but not hang together as coherent wholes. The bearing of observations on conclusions and generalizations seems somehow to have been missed. Sometimes answers to examination questions can be rich in information, but never really get to the point at issue. Learning to approach writing as a process could help students carry things through to a more complete result. For example, a student who has learned how to invest some effort in getting observations and notes organized on paper would come to class with an examination answer already "prewritten" to a significant extent. The writing done on the examination would be a recollection, an extension, and a refinement of that preparation.

Moreover, the "process" approach to writing stresses revision. Assignments are not written one time only but are revised to clarify and sharpen thought as it emerges. In successive drafts, teachers may well identify commonsense assumptions that interfere with students' grasp of science concepts and explanations. Revision may help students recognize and come to terms with these obstacles. Indeed, writing as a process can be such a useful means of developing coherent science understanding that some science teachers are beginning to assign longer-term projects that involve much more intermediate writing and lead to a more refined product than is usually the case in science classes.

Many science teachers, of course, are not prepared to help their students approach writing as this sort of process. In fact, the whole approach has only been developed in recent years. This difficulty might be overcome by collaborative work with English teachers in a high school. Such a writing-across-the-curriculum strategy could begin with students in a science class writing papers describing everything they did in preparing their most recent written work in the science class: examination, laboratory report, or longer-term project. Working with the science teacher, the English teacher would be able to analyze the students' accounts and identify the activities that had been most effective in preparing for the written work in science. Feedback from this analysis would help students strengthen their approach to writing in science and also begin to identify in a general way the strategies, particularly the prewriting activities, that seem most applicable to writing in the science class. If such an assessment were conducted on a regular basis, perhaps once during each year of high school, not only teachers but the students themselves would notice a gradual deepening of their ability to "think on paper." This, of course, is the potential payoff. Developing competence in writing for science classes could be a powerful support to developing integrated and coherent science understanding.

Speaking and Listening

Science teachers have properly attached great value to precise explanation. But if students are to develop the sorts of active understanding elaborated in Chapter 2, they must have the opportunity to formulate and express that understanding. Initially their expressions will be groping and tentative, not sharply drawn. It can be unwise to cut off such speech prematurely. Students' involvement with science requires careful cultivation. Further, because the development of science understanding involves refining and revising already held commonsense beliefs about the natural world, students need literally to come to terms with such preconceptions. Conversely, science teachers will need the chance to detect and engage those beliefs. That is to say, teachers can make use of greater opportunities to listen. This is a special sort of listening. As in observing the natural world, this listening involves interpretation, some attempt to make out the assumptions implied by what students are saying about natural phenomena.

We must also note the accumulating evidence that many teachers tend to ask the most able students to speak in class more often than other students. This inclination may keep the hypothetical ball rolling and ensure that what is said in class is close to what we hope for, but it does not provide all students the opportunities they need to formulate and express, to try out their emerging understanding of the natural world. *Academic Preparation in English* suggests the following ways in which teachers might work to engage more students in classroom discussion.

- Arrange for a videotaping of our class and analyze our teaching from the point of view of equitable interaction with all students. If technical assistance is not available, ask a trusted and experienced colleague to observe and provide feedback.

- Establish goals for involvement of specific students. We can, for example, preselect four or five students to whom we will, over several days, ask two or three questions designed to challenge and elicit significant responses.

- Maintain patience in building student competence through questioning. Students who have rarely been asked challenging questions will probably have little skill or interest in answering them: they and we can easily become discouraged. We must remember that competence comes slowly and that silence seldom means that nothing is happening. Experience indicates that the determination to ask is finally repaid by an equal determination to answer.

- Seek to have students frame and ask their own questions. If students rely entirely on questions asked by teachers, they will remain dependent learners. The ultimate purpose of the teacher is to encourage students to become independent learners. Students become independent—and thus responsible—to the extent that they formulate significant questions for which they desire to have answers.

As students are encouraged to formulate and express their own understanding of the natural world, that understanding is likely to become more precise and coherent.

VI. Toward Further Discussion

The illustrations and observations in this book are presented as suggestions. Often they are quite general; sometimes they aim at a point that will not be the crucial one in another situation. Adapting these suggestions and applying them in any particular set of circumstances will require further discussion among the science teachers concerned. Moreover, related to these suggestions about curriculum and instruction are many other issues that science teachers and those who work with them may want to consider. This concluding chapter highlights a few such further issues in the conviction that the telling discussion central to science and science education ought to extend to these other concerns as well.

Broadening the Range of Students Engaged in Science Learning

The goals of the Educational EQuality Project have a special relevance to science. In the perspectives taken and the suggestions offered in this book, we have tried to keep a special faith with those goals. Those who engage in scientific thought have always been a special group of people. We believe that this group should be much larger. The older methods of science education may have engaged as many students as they can. We need further discussion of how to develop the strengths and potential of all students.

This book has stressed that students come to the science classroom and laboratory already curious about natural phenomena, already holding ideas about the natural world. We have tried to suggest how engaging in the processes of scientific inquiry can help students refine and revise their beliefs about the natural world. In emphasizing the importance of descriptive and qualitative understanding in science, we also wanted to indicate that students' curiosity and interest in natural phenomena provide a starting point for engaging more of them in science learning. Overemphasizing the abstract varieties of science understanding can discourage rather than cultivate this interest. Virtually all students can be exploring, explaining, and testing explanations of natural phenomena. To a significant extent they already are. Our challenge as science teachers is to make the most of these beginnings and to expand them.

A further word needs to be said about the participation of women and minority students in science. Although in recent years the participation of women has increased noticeably, women and minority students are still vastly underrepresented in the study of science. Because the EQuality project is committed to improving the academic preparation of all students, we believe that this important matter merits a great deal of further attention. We suggest that discussion might usefully focus on the following topics:

- Ways to change a prevalent perception among many women and minority students that science and mathematics are alien, exclusive, and forbidding.
- Ways to instill in all students the notion that a career in a science-related field is rewarding and within reach, provided they continue their study in science and mathematics.
- Ways to engage and develop students' science understanding instead of emphasizing rote memorization.
- Ways to improve the quality of science and mathematics offerings in public schools that serve minority students.
- Ways to encourage parents' involvement and support in their children's science education.
- Ways that community-based organizations can support and supplement the work of schools and parents.

Making Room for Adequate Development of Skills and Understanding

This book, like *Academic Preparation for College*, suggests that the development of students' laboratory, field, and mathematical skills in the context of the several varieties of understanding should be central to high school instruction in science. We have already noted reason to believe that more students, given time and appropriate instruction, can achieve these learning outcomes. One problem is how to find that time in the face of a persistent tendency to overload the science curriculum. Scientific knowledge, of course, is expanding at an astonishing rate. One way to deal with these rapid advances in knowledge is to cram more and more material into the textbooks, adding a chapter or two to include the latest discoveries. A glance at most high school science textbooks quickly reveals that they are packed with information.

Like other knowledgeable observers, Michael O'Keefe, president of the Consortium for the Advancement of Private Higher Education, suggests that higher-quality education is mistakenly equated with "covering" a greater amount of material in a shorter time. While some students may be able to follow a lightning path through complex course materials, most students, though capable of mastering the material if it is presented at a reasonable pace, are left behind.

One solution is to teach less, but to teach it better. It is critical that teachers define carefully and parsimoniously what students need to learn. A textbook with 44 or so chapters, each of which deals with a fundamental area of a particular science field, is daunting, to say the least. A clear understanding of educational goals will make it easier to focus on needed topics, to delete others, and thus to reduce the amount of material treated to realistic proportions. Paring course material may also weaken the temptation to introduce students to long lists of vocabulary and definitions without context. A streamlined curriculum may, in fact, give teachers greater opportunity to stress fundamental concepts and to nurture the intellectual skills necessary to apprehend them.

Science teachers in a particular high school or school district may find it useful to consider how to reduce information overload in their particular curriculum. This problem will benefit from wider discussion as well. An important dimension in such discussion is not simply what teachers would like to teach. We all have our favorite topics. The crucial dimension is what content students need to learn. In a development that could complement *Academic Preparation for College*, the American Association for the Advancement of Science has launched the highly ambitious Project 2061. Its initial goal is to define in considerable detail the science, as well as technology and mathematics, content young people will need to learn. An additional note of realism may be brought to its deliberations by the inclusion of practicing scientists and engineers. Project 2061 holds the promise of helping to reduce curricular overload so that science learning can proceed more effectively. We look forward to its work and encourage science teachers to join in such discussions.

Determining Whether Students Attain the Learning Outcomes

We have suggested that curricular and instructional strategies could be regarded as hypotheses. If science education is considered in this light, then teachers in a given high school or school district will need to discuss whether or not the intended student learning is really taking place. In light of the previous discussion about broadening the range of students engaged successfully in science learning, an important dimension in any such discussion would be the proportion of students in a given high school or school district who are attaining the needed preparation in science. Moreover, it is important to gear instruction to the needs of the actual students in a given school or classroom. As illustrated in Chapter 4, instructional strategies can be targeted to specific learning outcomes, if such areas for special emphasis can be identified. That is to say, any means of assessment that teachers might employ could usefully be diagnostic as well as evaluative. Chapter 2 of this book analyzes the needed science learning outcomes into component parts. Such an analysis could be particularly useful in diagnostic assessment.

Encouraging Cooperation of Science and Mathematics Teachers

Mathematics and science teachers have a great deal to discuss. Science learning employs much of what mathematics teachers seek to develop. Conversely, mathematics teachers want to emphasize realistic applications of the sort that science can provide. Working with real science problems can help students consolidate their mathematics skills, particularly in such areas as estimation and approximation. Profitable discussion between science and mathematics teachers in a given high school can concern curricular coordination and the phased introduction of complementary concepts and applications.

Further, mathematics and science teachers share a common problem with respect to providing the needed academic preparation for all students. Indeed, it is inadequate preparation in mathematics that most often closes the door for minority and women students to enter careers in science and science-related fields. Teacher collaboration within a given high school, together with strong administrative leadership, can reverse this situation and create a climate in which all students are encouraged and enabled to prepare for a wider range of career opportunities. This problem does not end in high school, however. There is good reason for high school teachers to engage in further discussion with their higher education colleagues to make sure that the progress of minority and women students in science and mathematics does not stall on the other side of the academic transition.

Encouraging Cooperation of Science and Social Studies Teachers

We stressed earlier that the challenging future opened by scientific and technological developments needs to be addressed by the authentic voices of both science on the one side and history and the social sciences on the other. Absent either of these voices, without understanding of both science and society, thorough discussion of such issues is not likely to occur. Moreover, science teachers are trained to teach science; grappling alone with social issues would take them into an area where their own preparation could be subject to question. At the same time, science-related social issues are too important to be ignored. This is powerful reason for collaboration. Science and social studies teachers might consider both how special elective courses might be coordinated and how to address such issues in extracurricular settings.

Science and social studies teachers will find other common ground. Both wrestle with the problem of information overload; both need to find ways to restrict the information presented in their courses and to employ larger unifying concepts to help students deal coherently with large bodies of knowledge. Social studies teachers increasingly face the need to develop students' ability to employ quantitative methods. They, as well as science teachers, have reason to encourage the incorporation of statistics into the high school curriculum. Science teachers may be helpful also when social studies teachers consider when and how to use computer simulations in their courses.

Attracting and Retaining Well-trained Science Teachers

If science teachers feel inadequately rewarded for their important work, they are not unique. Many teachers in other fields feel the same way. A difference may be that many science teachers have attractive alternatives. This fact, together with the increasingly recognized economic importance of science and mathematics education, makes it possible to focus wider attention on the issue of adequate reward for teachers. The financial issue is not one that teachers can effectively discuss only among themselves. Increasingly, however, community and business leaders in some places are coming to appreciate that the public must pay for what it needs. It is important to recognize that the need for well-prepared teachers does not stop at school district lines, no more than the recruitment of well-educated employees stops there. In many cases, particularly those of school districts with limited financial resources, the question of adequate support for teachers must be addressed from a wider perspective. A similar point could be made about the financing of adequate and up-to-date laboratory equipment. Many state and business leaders now seem ready to join in such discussions.

We also want to suggest that the discussion of attracting and retaining well-prepared teachers does not stop with the financial question. Another important consideration is how to organize the conditions of work so that teachers can function as responsible professionals. Many officials need to join discussions concerning ways to make the most of the special knowledge that teachers bring to their work. How can the focus of a high school be kept on teaching and learning? How can teachers' professional judgments best be brought into play in shaping and refining educational programs? Such considerations indicate the importance of viewing science teaching as a profession and point to our concluding suggestion for discussion.

Arranging for Ongoing Discussion and Collaboration

Teachers can become isolated within their own classrooms and laboratories; yet the vitality of a profession springs from discussion and collaboration with colleagues. *Academic Preparation for College* was created by such discussion. The intent of this book is to extend the conversation that produced it to include many more teachers. Organizations of science teachers provide for such dialogue at the national and state levels, but such opportunities can seem remote from the daily work situation of the high school science teacher. The Yale–New Haven Teachers Institute, described in *Teaching in America: The Common Ground*, suggests one approach to ongoing collaboration among high school and college teachers in a particular city.[1]

Creating arrangements for ongoing discussion and collaboration among science teachers is particularly important in the context of this book. Here we have suggested that teachers join together, not just to teach science well but to undertake the even more challenging work of doing so for all students. To a significant extent, this work will carry science teachers into new ground. There will be many possibilities to investigate, many findings to report, many revisions to consider. This entire book was intended to begin a conversation about the crucial matter of democratic excellence in education. Its final suggestion for discussion must be that science teachers consider ways of continuing that conversation.

---

1. *Teaching in America: The Common Ground* (New York: College Entrance Examination Board, 1985).

Bibliography

The following publications may stimulate further discussion of issues and viewpoints featured in *Academic Preparation in Science* and provide suggestions for up-to-date instructional materials.

Anderson, Norman A., and Ronald D. Simpson. *Science, Students, and Schools*. New York: John Wiley & Sons, 1981. A broad coverage of methods for teaching middle and high school science. Detailed illustrations of various instructional strategies supplement the examples in Chapter 4 of this book. The treatments of inquiry techniques and techniques for individualizing instruction are particularly interesting.

Ausubel, David P., Joseph D. Novak, and Helen Hanesian. *Educational Psychology: A Cognitive View*. 2d ed. New York: Holt, Rinehart and Winston, 1978. A thorough presentation of educational psychology as an independent applied discipline dealing with the nature, outcomes, and evaluation of classroom learning from a cognitive viewpoint, a perspective employed in this book. Many of the illustrations deal directly with science teaching.

Champagne, Audrey B., and Leopold E. Klopfer. "Research in Science Education: The Cognitive Psychology Perspective." In *Redesigning Science and Technology Education: 1984 Yearbook*, ed. R. Bybee, J. Carlson, and A. McCormack. National Science Teachers Association, Washington, D.C., 1984. Discusses several key features of the cognitive psychology perspective on human learning and illustrates the relevance of this perspective for science teaching and learning. This brief essay shows how notions like cognitive structure, schemas in memory, and students' alternative conceptions relate to the teaching of science.

Gowin, D. Bob, and Joseph D. Novak. *Learning How to Learn*. New York: Cambridge University Press, 1984. The authors are particularly concerned about helping students to become more effective learners. Many of their ideas can be directly applied to students' learning of science. Offers a detailed guide to the classroom use of concept maps and Vee maps, introduced in Chapter 4 of this book.

Kaplan, Eugene H. *Problem Solving in Biology*. 3d ed. New York: Macmillan, 1983. This laboratory manual provides 33 individual explorations into the world of biological problem solving that emphasize the nature of scientific inquiry, rather than treating science as only a collection of facts and principles. The titles of some of Kaplan's laboratory exercises almost match several outcome components discussed in Chapter 2 of this book.

Karplus, Robert, Anton E. Lawson, Warren Wollman, Marilyn Appel, Robert Bernoff, Ann Howe, John J. Rusch, and Frank Sullivan. *Science Teaching and the Development of Reasoning: A Workshop*. 4 vols.: biology, chemistry, earth science, and physics. Berkeley, California: Regents of the University of California, 1977. Karplus and his colleagues prepared a series of guides for workshops to help teachers understand (1) how their students think and learn science content, (2) reasoning strategies employed by their students, and (3) instructional strategies designed to help students attain more advanced reasoning skills.

Schwab, Joseph J. "The Teaching of Science as Enquiry." In *The Teaching of Science*, ed. Joseph J. Schwab and Paul F. Brandwein. Cambridge, Massachusetts: Harvard University Press, 1962. Though published more than 20 years ago, this incisive analysis of the science curriculum and needed reforms is still relevant. Schwab's eight specific suggestions, with extended examples, of how science can be taught as enquiry provide valuable stimuli for thought and possible imitation. Included are the laboratory in an enquiry mode, the enquiring classroom, original scientific papers as curriculum materials, and narratives of enquiry.

Appendix A

Outcomes of precollege science education from *Academic Preparation for College.*

Laboratory and Field Work

- The ability to distinguish between scientific evidence and personal opinion by inquiry and questioning. (characterizes Outcomes A through F)
- The ability to recognize the role of observation and experimentation in the development of scientific theories. (Outcome E)
- Sufficient familiarity with laboratory and field work to ask appropriate scientific questions and to recognize what is involved in experimental approaches to the solutions of such questions. (Outcome B)
- The skills to gather scientific information through laboratory, field, and library work. (Outcome A)
- The ability to organize and communicate the results obtained by observation and experimentation. (Outcome C)

Mathematical Skills

- A quantitative understanding of at least one field of science—an understanding that employs the basic mathematical proficiency for all college entrants outlined in the foregoing description of learning outcomes in mathematics.
- The ability to interpret data presented in tabular and graphic form. (Outcome C)
- The ability to draw conclusions or make inferences from data. (Outcome D)
- The ability to select and apply mathematical relationships to scientific problems. (Outcome D)
- The ability to use mathematical relationships to describe results obtained by observation and experimentation. (Outcome C)
- The ability to interpret, in nonmathematical language, relationships presented in mathematical form. (Outcome C)

Fundamental Concepts

- Understanding in some depth of the unifying concepts of the life and physical sciences such as cell theory, geological evolution, organic evolution, atomic structure, chemical bonding, and transformations of energy. (Outcome F)

Detailed Knowledge

College entrants will need detailed knowledge of at least one field of science, ordinarily the field in which they have a quantitative understanding. This detailed knowledge could be in the earth sciences or in one of the newer, interdisciplinary fields of science. It could also be in one of the more traditional fields: biology, chemistry, or physics.

Appendix B

Excerpt from "The Web of Life"[1]

The Foundations of Life

Now let us replace rabbit and raspberry bush with another image: a cow chewing its cud in a meadow. Flies hover around the cow's ears; grasshoppers nibble the pasture grasses; birds pick off the grasshoppers; beetles bury the cow's dung. The image spreads like the ripples from a stone thrown into a pond. You can begin with *any* single living thing and, to a greater or lesser extent, develop beautiful strings of relationships. Biology begins at any place and leads in many directions, like a highway network on a map, like a spider's web.

Where shall we take hold of this web of life?

Whether we look at the individual or at the living world as a whole, we find that both the balance and the changes involve the flow of *energy* and *matter*. The details of the flow will develop throughout the rest of our biology course. In this chapter we wish only to look at the broad outline.

Energy

In every phase of life sketched in these preceding paragraphs, was there not some activity? The cow was chewing; the flies were flying; even the grass was actively growing; and the flowers in the meadow were opening in the sunshine.

Now activity always requires energy. Whenever anything *happens*, energy is involved. Physicists a long time ago developed an important principle called the Conservation of Energy: "Energy can neither be created nor destroyed." Although physicists have since found that matter and energy are interchangeable under certain conditions, life is not possible under these conditions. Therefore, whenever you see some biological activity, you can ask, "Where does the energy come from?"

Source of energy. Where does *your* energy come from? No doubt you have been urged to eat in order to grow and in order to play or to work— in other words, to be active.

---

1. From "The Web of Life" chapter in Biological Sciences Curriculum Study, BSCS Green Version, *Biological Science: An Ecological Approach*, 2d ed. (Chicago: Rand McNally, 1968), pp. 18–20.

It may require some imagination to look at a potato and see energy in it—or even a hamburger and see in it the winning touchdown of the big game. For present purposes we need only point out that energy is not involved in activity *only*; it may be present when there is merely the *possibility* of activity. An automobile runs. There is activity—energy. The gasoline sits in the tank. The gasoline is not active, but the activity of the car is derived from it. Therefore we say that the gasoline contains energy. The energy in the gasoline is called *chemical* energy. Such energy is found in the bonds that hold together the atoms within the molecules of a substance. The potato and the hamburger also contain chemical energy in the bonds of their molecules: you can use this energy in your life activities.

Where does the chemical energy in the substances that consumers eat come from? Remember: we are operating under the physicists' principle that energy cannot be created under conditions in which life exists. So the question "Where from?" is inescapable. By this question we are led from one part of the web to another.

Suppose we consider the hamburger. It is made of meat that was once part of a cow. But where did the cow get the energy? It, too, must consume substances that already contain chemical energy—substances from other organisms. Nothing in its animal body allows for any other form of energy-capture. We animals—men, cows, lions—are all consumers. But the cow differs from the lion in one important way: the cow does not consume another animal; it consumes grass or grain. Like the rabbit, it is a first-order consumer, while lions are second-order consumers—as we are when we eat hamburgers.

The grass plant and the potato plant do not consume any other organism; they do not "eat." Then where does the green plant's energy come from? You know—from light. It is a little difficult to show that light can directly produce activity, but someone from the physics class may be able to demonstrate this. At any rate, light is a form of energy, and it supplies the energy for most plants. And the source of this light energy is the sun.

Members of the Council on Academic Affairs, 1983-85

Peter N. Stearns, Heinz Professor of History, Carnegie-Mellon University, Pittsburgh, Pennsylvania (*Chair* 1983-85)

Dorothy S. Strong, Director of Mathematics, Chicago Public Schools, Illinois (*Vice Chair* 1983-85)

Victoria A. Arroyo, College Board Student Representative, Emory University, Atlanta, Georgia (1983-84)

Ida S. Baker, Principal, Cape Coral High School, Florida (1984-85)

Michael Anthony Brown, College Board Student Representative, University of Texas, Austin (1983-85)

Jean-Pierre Cauvin, Associate Professor of French, Department of French and Italian, University of Texas, Austin (1983-84)

Alice C. Cox, Assistant Vice President, Student Academic Services, Office of the President, University of California (1983-84, Trustee Liaison 1984-85)

Charles M. Dorn, Professor of Art and Design, Department of Creative Arts, Purdue University, West Lafayette, Indiana (1983-84)

Sidney H. Estes, Assistant Superintendent, Instructional Planning and Development, Atlanta Public Schools, Georgia (1983-85)

David B. Greene, Chairman, Division of Humanities, Wabash College, Crawfordsville, Indiana (1984-85)

Jan A. Guffin, Chairman, Department of English, North Central High School, Indianapolis, Indiana (1983-85)

John W. Kenelly, Professor of Mathematical Sciences, Clemson University, South Carolina (1983-85)

Mary E. Kesler, Assistant Headmistress, The Hockaday School, Dallas, Texas (Trustee Liaison 1983-85)

Arthur E. Levine, President, Bradford College, Massachusetts (1983-85)

Deirdre A. Ling, Vice Chancellor for University Relations and Development, University of Massachusetts, Amherst (Trustee Liaison 1983-84)

Judith A. Lozano-Loredo, Superintendent, Southside Independent School District, San Antonio, Texas (1983-84)

Eleanor M. McMahon, Commissioner of Higher Education, Rhode Island Office of Higher Education, Providence (1984-85)

Jacqueline Florance Meadows, Instructor of Social Science, North Carolina School of Science and Mathematics, Durham (1983-84)

Michael J. Mendelsohn, Professor of English, University of Tampa, Florida (1983-84)

Fay D. Metcalf, History Coordinator/Teacher, Boulder High School, Colorado (1983-85)

Vivian Rivera, College Board Student Representative, Adlai E. Stevenson High School, Bronx, New York (1984-85)

Raul S. Rodriguez, Chair, Language Department, Xaverian High School, Brooklyn, New York (1984-85)

Michael A. Saltman, Chairman, Science Department, Bronxville School, New York (1983-85)

Vivian H. T. Tom, Social Studies Teacher, Lincoln High School, Yonkers, New York (Trustee Liaison 1983-84)

Kenneth S. Washington, Vice Chancellor for Educational Services, Los Angeles Community College District, California (1983-85)

Henrietta V. Whiteman, Director/Professor, Native American Studies, University of Montana, Missoula (1984-85)

Roberto Zamora, Deputy Executive Director, Region One Education Service Center, Edinburg, Texas (1984-85)